Alignment

The Key to the Success of
The University of Maryland Medical System:
America's First Teaching Hospital

Alignment

The Key to the
Success of the
University of Maryland
Medical System:

America's First Teaching Hospital

Morton I. Rapoport, MD
Stephen C. Schimpff, MD

Design: Brushwood Graphics Design Group
Dust jacket design: Nancy Johnston
Printing: Schmitz Press

Underwritten by the University of Maryland Medical System and with
support from the Medical Alumni Association of the University of
Maryland, Inc.

ISBN-0-9619119-5-6
978-0-9619119-5-9

To our wives, Rosalie and Carol,
for their constant love and support

Contents

Foreword

This book is a history of the University of Maryland Medical System (UMMS), especially of its creation by the Maryland legislature in 1984 and the events that followed during the ensuing 25 years. It is our hope that we have both documented a remarkable transition of an ailing hospital into a highly regarded medical system and explained by example why alignment, adherence to the truth, and an entrepreneurial spirit are essential to success. But it has not been approached as a scholarly treatise. We have both written many scientific articles over the years where every fact was checked and referenced. That was not the approach we took here. This is a book based largely on our recollections, recollections of the times lived by the two of us and thus how we perceived the events that transpired. We believe them to be accurate. We did indeed contact many key individuals to confirm our memories, and we have included references to some important articles that are relevant to the main themes. In the end, our memories and our biases tempered the following pages. We therefore offer our views on what has happened over these years and have taken the liberty of expressing what we believe would be best for the continued success of the medical system, and for its sister institution, the University of Maryland School of Medicine, as well as the faculty physicians.

This book is more than just a history of a few years in the life of a particular medical institution; it's a compendium of lessons learned, lessons in how a medical system must be managed as a business yet led with its mission to care always foremost in mind. It offers the lesson that while leading and managing in an academic health center environment, it is necessary to develop alignments with faculty physicians, medical school leaders, the business community and key state government constituencies. This in turn requires recognizing the special needs of all the partners while keeping the critical agenda as the ultimate target; recognizing the other partners' legitimate needs and with that their personal and institutional agendas; accepting bad news as it comes and using the bad news to drive needed change; and concurrently recognizing reality even when reality is counter to current beliefs and directions. The truth needs to be verified as actual reality, but then it must be embraced and used to guide strategy and tactics.

What was known as the University of Maryland Hospital had, in the early 1980s, been failing for many years. The number of admissions had fallen; there were few private patients; the hospital was considered an "indigent care" institution; there had been no upgrades to the 1934 building which still did not have air conditioning and was replete with large multi-bed wards rather than patient rooms; radiology was woefully behind the times as were other technologies and laboratories; it was hard to recruit bright young physicians, and the local physicians in private practice that had previously brought their patients to University Hospital no longer did so; and with all of this, the hospital was losing money each year, was asking the state for supplemental appropriations to cover the shortfalls, had poor financial systems in place and had in many ways become a yoke weighing down on the university and its medical school.

It was in 1982 that the new chancellor, T. Albert Farmer, MD, decided it was time for a change in the way the hospital operated and asked Morton I. Rapoport, MD, to become the CEO of a restructured and renamed University of Maryland Medical System, a system that would be separated from state ownership and university governance two years later. Rapoport was Baltimore born and raised, had graduated from the University of Maryland School of Medicine and then spent six years in the U.S. Army including time conducting basic research at the Walter

Reed Army Institute of Research in Washington, D.C., and the U.S. Army Medical Research Institute for Infectious Diseases in Frederick, Md. He returned to the medical school as a faculty member in 1967, working in the infectious disease division of the department of medicine and in Shock Trauma as its first internist. Soon he was asked to become chief of medicine at the nearby affiliated Veterans Administration Hospital and then was promoted to professor and asked to become senior associate dean. It was this medical and leadership background along with the entrepreneurship taught him by his father (as he worked in the family grocery store as a child) that he brought with him to this new and challenging role.

One of his first recruits to a senior leadership position was Stephen C. Schimpff, MD. Schimpff had graduated from Yale Medical School, done his residency there in internal medicine, and in 1969 joined the Baltimore Cancer Research Center (BCRC) of the National Cancer Institute (NCI). There he conducted infectious disease research and clinical care among patients with advanced cancer and served as physician to patients with leukemia and lymphoma.

Schimpff and Rapoport met at that time with Rapoport acting as a teacher and mentor. Over time, Schimpff developed a research program that enlisted many people both in house and internationally, became head of infectious diseases and microbiology research in the NCI, and then head of infectious diseases for the medical school. The BCRC used rented space in University Hospital and the medical school research tower beginning in 1974, but in 1981 the NCI decided to close the BCRC. Rapoport, just appointed CEO of the medical system, and John Dennis, MD, dean of the medical school, decided to use the remnants of the BCRC to begin a cancer center for the University of Maryland. They asked Schimpff to become the first professor and director. There were major issues to overcome including developing a referral base, creating a practice plan, recruiting faculty and staff and starting a research program now to be based on grants and contracts rather than direct funding from the NCI. This was Schimpff's managerial and leadership challenge and his training ground for the next three-plus years.

By 1985 the new medical system was functioning better than before, but Rapoport still needed a senior managerial partner. The cancer center had progressed well under Schimpff's leadership, and so Rapoport asked that he join him as executive vice president and COO. Thus was the partnership of the two of us created, a partnership that persisted until we both retired in 2003. By then, over 20 years since its creation, the new medical system was financially stable and indeed strong, University Hospital had been largely recapitalized and rebuilt as the University of Maryland Medical Center with modern buildings and technology allowing for the recruitment of outstanding faculty physicians and excellent staff who in turn created superb patient care programs; the system had grown to include seven hospitals; and combined the system accounted for a very large share of the hospitalized patients in the region and state along with an annual budget of about $2 billion.

We are proud of the changes that took place over this time period and have thus developed this book to document what was necessary to allow the successes to occur.

The approaches to leadership and management which we used are relevant not only to a particular hospital at a moment in time but also to academic medical centers and hospitals in general and to business and political leadership in many settings and places. Throughout this book we emphasize the importance of alignment for a hospital to achieve excellent outcomes with other critical organizations such as the state government, the university, the medical school, the faculty physicians and others. By alignment we mean assuring a level of congruence between the medical system and medical school, the university, the rate setting commission, the governors and the legislature regarding vision, strategy and agendas. A metaphor may help explain our concept. A person's spine must have each of the vertebrae "aligned" one atop the other. Without this alignment, the person stoops over, develops respiratory insufficiency and other medical ills impairing normal function and indeed the person's very life itself. So too then must an academic hospital or hospital system align with its key partners and stakeholders lest it no longer can remain upright and functional.

We also emphasize the importance of an entrepreneurial spirit and approach to management; the need for vision setting, strategy development and prioritization. And we discuss how freeing the hospital from state ownership and university governance allowed the other leadership and management principles to be effective. We therefore describe our approach and methods using both a "dry" institutional history and some, perhaps more intriguing, personal vignettes to make particular points.

Morton I. Rapoport, MD
Stephen C. Schimpff, MD
Fall, 2009

Acknowledgments

Many individuals assisted us throughout the development of this manuscript. We interviewed too many individuals to list here by name, but their contributions are gratefully appreciated. The following reviewed various drafts of the manuscript and made numerous suggestions for improvement: James Kagan, senior consultant of Chartis Consulting; Richard Knapp, special assistant to the president, Association of American Medical Colleges; James Bentley, executive vice president of the American Hospital Association; Spencer Foreman, MD, retired CEO of Montefiore Hospital, New York City; Nathan Schnaper, professor and head of psychiatry services for the Greenebaum Cancer Center; and Charles Seashore, PhD, organizational development consultant.

Jerry Wollman, RN, MBA, reviewed the manuscript and developed specific information needed for completeness and accuracy. Robert Chrencik, UMMS CEO made numerous suggestions about alignment at other academic medical centers. John Ashworth reminded us of much of the Shock Trauma history and reviewed sections of the manuscript as did Mark Wasserman. James Dale made useful suggestions in the early development of concepts. Margaret Frazier transcribed Schimpff's dictations, and helped in myriad ways over the course of manuscript development. Nancy Jackson, former copy editor for the *Baltimore Sun*, copy edited the manuscript. Amy Meyers of the UMMS finance staff reviewed the financial materials and developed the data for the graphics. Milford Foxwell, MD, assistant dean for admissions at the medical school, helped with the early history of the Baltimore Infirmary and University Hospital. Gregory Handlir, associate dean for resource management of the school of medicine, offered the financial and grants data of the school of medicine. Carolyn McGuire-Frenkil provided early moral and financial support to get the project started. Larry Pitrof, executive director of the alumni association, was an early supporter and offered major encouragement to develop the book along with assistance over the 18 months of effort. Morton Krieger, MD, edited the manuscript at its completion and made our writing styles not only readable but interesting. Nancy Johnston expertly and artistically designed the book.

We also wish to acknowledge, without offering specific names, all those who worked with us—physicians, nurses, support staff, managers at all levels—to create and develop the medical system as it is today.

Most importantly we need to thank Rosalie Rapoport and Carol Schimpff. Not only were they supportive during the preparation of this book, but they have been our support systems over the years. Whenever times were tough, and that was frequently, they were there to offer encouragement, advice and wisdom. We owe them much for our successes; our failures are our own responsibilities.

CHAPTER ONE

Introduction

Academic medical centers (AMCs) consisting of a school of medicine, a faculty practice plan and a teaching hospital are a critical element in the nation's healthcare delivery system. They provide residency training for about 75% of the country's physicians, provide almost one-half of the charity care given to the poor and under-insured, operate the most intense care units such as neonatal and pediatric intensive care, and are the sites of most of the clinical research in this country that brings forth new approaches to medical care. These are institutions that are always straining under the need for added resources as the costs of care increase, the need for training programs accelerates and the principles of quality and safety demand more and more attention. Over the years, various stresses have led AMCs to look at their structure and governance mechanisms and consider whether changes are needed in order to advance these vital institutions into the future. Such was the case at the University of Maryland School of Medicine during the latter part of the 20th century.

By the early 1980s, University Hospital, which admitted about 21,000 mostly indigent patients annually, was losing money and had a physical plant that was deteriorating and outdated, specifically in the areas of diagnostic and therapeutic technology, cardiac catheterization and information systems. The physicians, all faculty members of the medical school, focused largely on teaching, considering patient care a necessary element of that teaching mission; the attraction of private patients was not considered essential or even desirable. Two new research buildings had recently been opened, and the school was now in the position of attracting bright young scientists to develop the research agenda. This had begun in the basic science departments but had not progressed to the clinical departments, in large part because recruitment of talented clinician-scientists was limited by the deficiencies in the hospital, and also because it was not considered a priority by many of the senior faculty leaders. The school of medicine in 1984 had 710 faculty; sponsored research amounted to $35 million; and the practice plan was a hodge-podge of individual plans run by departments and divisions without a centralized structure. Change was badly needed.

How did we get started? What were the key drivers that allowed success to occur? A series of themes will thus dominate the text. The first theme is alignment with the school of medicine and its clinical faculty. Alignment was essential since the only way forward was with these two partners. Indeed, the original hospital was paid for and built in 1823 by the faculty to extend their educational mission. The medical system had to be a vital partner of the school and the faculty, and vice versa; so that

The Baltimore Infirmary, 1823

all could prosper and develop to their fullest potentials. As we will emphasize again and again throughout the text, alignment has been critical for success even if not always appreciated by the partners, especially in the early years after privatization.

This alignment theme also relates to the issue that although separate governance (i.e., separation from state ownership and university governance) was essential, the medical system as created was a "negative asset" as related to facilities and technology. The result was that no amount of effective management could overcome the deficiencies. It was impossible to "bootstrap" adequate capital to rebuild the institution. The state was needed to recapitalize or at least join in a public-private partnership to assist in recapitalization. Here again alignment was critical, alignment with the state government including the governor and key legislative members. Alignment with business leaders and donors who had important ties to the state government and to the medical system proved highly useful. And alignment with the university at large since it had its own extensive capital needs and those of UMMS could be perceived as competitive with that of the university. Finally, there was a need to partner or align with the agenda of the state regulator that set hospital rates in order to achieve the necessary rate structures in return for attention to costs and, later, quality. As it turned out, once these alignment processes were started and the public-private partnership with the state instituted, UMMS was able to maximize and magnify the results. But the key step for us was to accept accountability for the medical system's success (or failure) and no longer assume that responsibility rested elsewhere.

Alignment can be about developing close personal relationships with one's counter partners in the key related organizations. While this can be very important, we refer here to alignment as related to strategies, priorities, agendas, decision structures and other institutional structures. Good alignment allows leveraging strategies as this book will demonstrate. Positive personal relationships can only enhance collaboration but cannot be exchanged for the substance of alignment. It must be noted that the importance of alignment was not always recognized over the years, and the leaders of the new system and university lost sight of its importance from time to time.*

The second theme is the way in which an entrepreneurial orientation helped to create a marked shift from past management approaches. First and foremost was the need to be accountable, to accept that success (or failure) was the responsibility of the leadership, not of others. It meant a "bottom line" focus with value judgments and cost benefit judgments; the types of judgments that are not always "natural" for physicians and other health care providers. And yet this focus had to be in the context of the mission—to care for patients, to educate the next generation of health care providers and to foster clinical research and discovery. This reconciliation of mission with entrepreneurial needs was not always easy but it was critical to success.

The third theme consists of employing leadership, vision, management, a clear strategy and priority setting to bring vitality, dynamism and respect with solid financial results, high-quality, world-class programs and regional respect to a failing hospital. This leadership forged new directions, departing from the old; envisioned a preferred state and how to get there; created a management team and management philosophy to achieve the vision; and developed a clear strategy for all to follow.

The fourth theme, of course, emphasizes a model of public-private collaboration built on a corporate platform of governance and structure, yet affiliated with state government. Certain functions are not inherently governmental—the running of an academic medical center is one of them. That is not to say that government cannot or should not operate hospitals; it can and does. The question was should it in this instance? The eventual determination by those involved was "No."

*The term alignment has been used by other authors in a different context. For example, alignment can refer to internal alignment of all members of a business to focus on the main objectives of the company. This type of alignment within a company is vital, but is different from our usage here.[1, 2]

NOTES:

1. Labovitz, G and Rosansky, V "The Power of Alignment: How Great Companies Stay Centered and Accomplish Extraordinary Things," Wiley, 1997
2. Kaplan, RS and Norton, DP "Alignment: Using the Balanced Scorecard to Create Corporate Synergies" Harvard Business Press, 2006

This story begins with a mediocre medical institution, run like a state entity, which no matter how much state money was invested, still ran deficits and had a poor physical plant and unsatisfying conditions for all. Freeing the hospital from state ownership and university governance allowed the focus on alignment, an entrepreneurial approach to management, and a leadership approach to create a vision and strategy for success.

This then will illustrate the transformation of University Hospital of the early 1980s using an entrepreneurial management approach, vision and strategy leadership and especially alignment following separate governance to achieve a dynamic system that is today regionally recognized for the quality of its healing, teaching and discovery.

CHAPTER TWO

Why Privatize University Hospital?

A hospital is an enterprise and so needs to be managed in an entrepreneurial manner with strategic direction, innovation and sound management. An academic hospital can only function well if its mission and leadership are closely aligned with the mission and leadership of its associated school of medicine. For many years, these criteria had not been met at University Hospital. An historical review will set the stage.

The history of the medical system begins in 1807 with the creation of what is now the University of Maryland Medical School. The school was the fifth in the country and the first to be created independently, not as part of an overall university. Indeed the current University System of Maryland and its 13 campuses across the state grew out of the original school of medicine. Medicine in the early 1800s was practiced in the doctor's office or at home. Hospitals, except for the insane, largely did not exist. In 1823 the faculty decided they needed a hospital to teach their students. The cornerstone was laid June 10, and the building completed October 20, funded by a $7,000 loan secured by the faculty, who contributed another $7,000 directly to pay the balance of the $14,000 costs. The new Baltimore Infirmary was thus owned by the seven contributing physicians and remained that way for many years. It was also the first general hospital in Baltimore, consisting of 60 beds with nursing care provided by the Sisters of Charity from Mount St. Mary's in Emmitsburg, Md. The Baltimore Infirmary was the first hospital built in the United States specifically for medical education. Medical students had a place to sleep in the building, and they had much of their clinical education there. The first "resident physician" as we would now call the position was employed in 1846. In the 1850s the Baltimore Infirmary was enlarged to 150 beds, becoming the largest hospital in the city. During the Civil War it was used by the Union Army as a hospital (with added tents) for patients on the grounds. Maryland was a border state, with substantial southern sympathies, and many key battles were fought in Maryland and in nearby Virginia. The hospital offered beds to the federal government for $5 per week for a wounded soldier, more than the $3 per week required of other private patients. Then, in 1876, the legislature funded a new wing and in 1890 another wing was built for a nurses' home.

The Baltimore Infirmary was demolished after 73 years in 1897 and replaced by a new building named, for the first time, University Hospital. This five-story building had 200 beds and was built over a 13-month

University Hospital, 1897

period. As with the original hospital, this one was funded by the medical faculty through a bond issue that came due in 1936, although the state later gave funds for a new nurses' home, a power facility and some additions that raised the bed count to 250. In 1920, a state university was formed when the regents of the University of Maryland and the Trustees of the Maryland State College of Agriculture agreed to consolidate. Both institutions turned their property over to the state. University Hospital was now no longer a private institution but rather owned by the state and governed by the regents of the university.

In 1931 the state appropriated $31.5 million, which along with some private donations, was used to build the new University Hospital,

University Hospital, 1934

opened in 1934 with a 400-bed capacity. Considered an architectural masterpiece, it won numerous design awards. The old University Hospital building became the outpatient clinic. In 1953, the recognition that many patients with mental illness were getting unacceptable care—the "shame of Maryland" as one newspaper put it—necessitated a 185-bed addition to the new hospital to house the Maryland Institute of Psychiatry and Human Behavior, a new concept in psychiatric care. A large 13-story addition, which came to be known as the north hospital, was completed in 1973 bringing the bed capacity to about 800. This building also included six floors for ambulatory care, resulting in the demolition of the 1897 building. Although opened in 1973, it was first designed in the 1950s and delayed in the 1960s; so when eventually built it was 20 years behind the times. Further, budget constraints at the time led to such design changes as substantially reducing the number of elevators—a decision that would plague the hospital for decades to come. During this same time period, a grant from the federal government supported construction of the first Shock Trauma building adjoining University Hospital in 1968. These buildings, along with some support facilities, became the University of Maryland Medical System in 1982.

Today, all that remains of the 1823 Baltimore Infirmary is one of the granite steps now placed in the current main entrance, and a marble block from the 1897 University Hospital, also imbedded in the current buildings.

In the 1970s University Hospital faced issues of uncontrolled cost escalations; an ambiguity of leadership between the hospital, the medical school and the university; an uncertain or even absence of accountability; inadequate management information systems such as payroll, personnel and accounting; an aging of assets; a duplication of resources; uneven quality at best; and a woeful absence of newer technologies, such as CT scanners and sophisticated equipment in the clinical laboratories.

Within this framework, the vision for University Hospital developed over the years, driven largely by the faculty of the school of medicine and particularly its leading department chairs. They perceived that the purpose of the faculty was to teach, and therefore the purpose of the hospital was as a venue for teaching just as it had been when founded in 1823. Although patient care was important and critical it essentially was undertaken by the faculty for the purpose of teaching students.

The years after World War II brought many changes to American medical schools. One change nationally was the growth and importance of the National Institutes of Health (NIH) and the monies that were available from it for research grants and contracts. These available dollars led many medical schools to rapidly strengthen their research capabilities with facilities and faculty in order to apply for the NIH monies. Private medical schools like Harvard, Yale, Johns Hopkins and Stanford were leaders followed by some of the state university schools of medicine such as the University of California San Francisco, the University of Washington, the University of Alabama and others. This was the time when the career track that became known as clinician-scientist blossomed, and these individuals later became the leaders of many medical schools or key departments across the country. But the University of Maryland School of Medicine was not to become one of them to any substantial degree during those early post-war years. The few highly regarded researchers were the exception to the rule of clinician-educators. No school leaders stepped up to try to attract clinician-scientists. Admittedly, the school had limited laboratory space available, but neither was there an apparent effort to develop more space at that time.

Another change, also occurring nationally, related to faculty. Traditionally, as in most medical schools of the time, volunteers did most of the teaching by involving students in the care of their patients admitted to University Hospital. Many of Baltimore's finest physicians, with offices in the upscale neighborhoods around the Washington Monument, were volunteer faculty. But after WWII, there was a trend to first hire full-time department chairmen and then recruit what we will call geographic full-time faculty. Over time the vision of this senior faculty was that it was better to have geographic full-time faculty than volunteer faculty for the purpose of student teaching. As a result the volunteer physicians were not "protected" or "honored." Over time the volunteers admitted fewer and fewer of their patients to University Hospital, choosing the more hospitable and renovated hospitals in central Baltimore, such as Mercy, Union Memorial or Maryland General. Soon they were no longer a significant force among the faculty. With this turn of events, the housestaff (residents and interns) "ran" the hospital care programs, an arrangement which the faculty, as at many academic medical centers of the time, found advantageous. This allowed the faculty more time for other activities without the requirements of direct patient care.

In the late 1960s a department of medicine resident who had graduated from the Johns Hopkins School of Medicine observed to Rapoport that University Hospital was a "resident-run hospital;" one that as a result, he felt, was quite different from the Johns Hopkins Hospital across town. He noted that the University Hospital residents did a lot of procedures and made substantial decisions without faculty supervision. The teaching he felt was excellent, but the care was not as good as it could be or should be as a result of the lack of intense faculty supervision.

With the housestaff favoring the full-time faculty, the hospital, essentially by default, tended to exclude the private practitioners. Since the full-time faculty members did not have substantial personal private practices, University Hospital had become primarily an indigent care hospital, a slow, progressive change that occurred during the 1950s through the 1970s. This in turn led to a decline in admissions and a further increase in the percentage of indigent patients in the hospital. This was quite different from Johns Hopkins Hospital, where the tradition of private voluntary attending staff was retained and, indeed, was considered essential to the hospital's function and its teaching mission. A highly respected faculty member was placed in charge of the private teaching service with separate arrangements for housestaff and a separate section of the hospital. As a result Johns Hopkins maintained its admissions from private physicians, and these amounted to at least 20% of overall admissions to the hospital, as they do to this day. So, the University of Maryland School of Medicine had few volunteers teaching students through the care of their patients in the University Hospital, nor did it have many clinician-scientists on the full-time faculty, and it had not developed substantial research programs funded by the NIH—as did many of its prestigious counterparts across the country.

This began to change with the recruitment of new clinical leadership who differed in perspective. For years the established protocol was to appoint insiders to lead departments when a chair retired. John Moxley, MD, dean of the medical school from 1969 to 1973, broke that tradition. Moxley, who had roots in Baltimore, was recruited from Harvard School of Medicine after time at the NIH. He recruited chairs from other academic medical centers so as to bring in fresh ideas and an understanding of how other medical schools were changing.

Over time and with new clinical leadership, these forces began to change. An example was the recruitment from Duke University of M. Carlyle Crenshaw, MD, to head obstetrics and gynecology in the late 1970s. On his first day of work he assembled his faculty and announced, "I will stay in the hospital overnight tonight; which of you will take tomorrow night?" This was a dramatic change to have a faculty member in attendance throughout the night. In the department of obstetrics and gynecology it raised a lot of eyebrows and, indeed, some faculty left to work elsewhere, not liking the new approach.

Meanwhile University Hospital was suffering major annual financial losses. During Governor Marvin Mandel's term (1969 to 1979), he had a meeting with a business friend who told him that he would no longer send any of his employees to the University of Maryland Hospital.

"Why?" asked the governor.

The response was, "Well, I guess the care is okay, but the business operations are terrible. They have never sent me a bill for services for my patients. I know that I have a large account payable, and I don't even know how much it is. I can't run my business this way, and they should not do so either."

Such was the view within the business community, and that view was becoming known to the governor and the legislature. This type of report added to the frustration of the state government that the hospital, through the university, would come "hat in hand" each year to ask for additional money for one reason or another, such as preparation for the joint commission survey. It seemed that the hospital was never able to make things function without added help each year; no matter what was budgeted the previous spring.

A substantial addition to the hospital had been planned in the 1950s but had been set aside by the state. In general, the Baltimore campus was not "high" on the list of priorities for capital funding. But hospital director George H. Yeager, MD, was able to impress the governor and legislature of the need, and hence the north hospital was completed in 1973, nearly doubling the bed capacity and creating an entire new area for outpatient services. Yeager retired upon its opening. During this same time frame, Moxley, working with Chancellor Albin Kuhn, was able to get state approval for two new medical school research towers, one opening in 1975 and one in 1978. These dollars came about in part as a result of federal decisions to enhance the ranks of primary care physicians by funding growth of medical school enrollments and by encouraging the development of new medical schools. Maryland benefitted, and the state provided the dollars for the new buildings.

The general practice was for the state to collect the hospital revenues yet separately set an annual operating budget. The two did not necessarily have any relation to each other. This meant that there was no incentive for the hospital staff to bill and collect or to manage budgets so as to generate a surplus to use for equipment purchases or renovations. The state systems for purchasing and personnel were complex, to say the least, and resulted in slowness of action at a time of increased competition among hospitals in the region. Indeed, the legislature made the systems even more restrictive after former governor and then U.S. Vice President Spiro T. Agnew was indicted for accepting bribes, largely from contractors. Obtaining even minor capital dollars for renovations and repairs was now a complex process, taking years to get approvals. The "three Ps" of personnel, purchasing and physical plant had thus become overwhelming burdens for the hospital.

In the 1970s the State of Maryland created the Health Services Cost Review Commission (HSCRC). It had a multi-part mission to control the spiraling increase in costs across the hospitals in Maryland, to create a mechanism to deal with uncompensated care; so that everyone would be afforded hospital care without the need for charity hospitals and, third, to maintain viability of well-run hospitals. The initial director of the HSCRC was Harold Cohen, PhD, who, with his staff, was quick to point out that University Hospital was high cost but was not able to demonstrate a higher level of quality to go with that level of cost. Indeed, University Hospital was by far the most costly hospital in Maryland! The commission set in motion efforts to rein in those costs but was hampered by the fact that the hospital was not able to respond to its request for improved accounting procedures.

By 1980, University Hospital was enduring annual financial losses and had a growing inability to collect what it was owed. Articles ran in the Baltimore newspapers describing offices where one could open drawers and literally find them full of patient accounts that had never been billed. Yet here was the hospital asking the HSCRC for higher rates when they were not even collecting what the commission had already approved. Admissions which had been declining, continued on a downward spiral. The facilities, built primarily in the mid 1930s (the south hospital building), the mid 1950s (the psychiatric institute), and the early 1970s (the north hospital) were in poor repair and frankly inadequate for what was deemed modern levels of care and technology at the time. The technology base of the hospital was woefully deficient; the only CT scanner came from the NCI, which had put it in at the hospital to do studies of malignant brain tumors. Other technology in the department of radiology was at least ten years old and usually substantially older than that. The clinical laboratories were likewise outmoded as were the cardiac catheterization laboratories, and there were no acceptable procedure suites for pulmonary testing or gastrointestinal endoscopy.

No one was satisfied. University officials, needing to focus on their educational mission, found University Hospital a burden at best. Medical school leaders felt likewise but also recognized the importance of the hospital for its teaching mission. State officials were highly frustrated by the financial status, and the HSCRC staff and commissioners saw a hospital unable to respond to their requirements. It was within this environment that the consideration of privatizing the hospital arose. From a governance perspective it would free the hospital from state personnel and purchasing requirements that drove up the costs of care in an era of cost management. It would also mean that the hospital could have its own board of trustees who would focus principally on the mission of clinical care and not be distracted, so to speak, by the necessities of what was then a 13-campus university across the entire state of Maryland. Despite these perceived advantages, there were significant concerns about privatization, particularly about mission. Would a separate corporation still honor the requirements for the medical school's teaching needs and also for its faculty's clinical research activities? But at heart, the most important issues driving the thoughts about privatizing the hospital were achieving accountability, fixing quality issues and developing functioning systems while finding a mechanism for conflict resolution.

The forces for change included the University System of Maryland Board of Regents, state legislature, and the HSCRC but the most important was Farmer, the newly appointed chancellor. Farmer had been recruited from the University of Tennessee in Memphis by University of Maryland president John S. Toll, PhD. Farmer's charge from Toll was to resolve the many conflicts on the University of Maryland at Baltimore (UMAB) campus, such as the leadership struggles between the school of medicine and Shock Trauma, as well as the status of University Hospital.

Although everyone knew that something needed to be done with University Hospital to improve it, some forces opposed a radical change like separate governance. The school essentially liked the status quo wherein the director of the hospital reported to the dean. Toll wanted to be rid of the problem but at the same time wanted to maintain the hospital under university control. Basically the medical school department chairs (also chiefs of service in University Hospital) along with the dean, the president of the university system and others did not want true separation. What they preferred was to have the state government uninvolved in the hospital and its management.

The real and underlying issue was that no one wanted to effectively "own" the myriad problems that frustrated state officials. In short the usual message was that the problems were the doings of other parties. To illustrate the type of mentality that was rife within the institution,

Schimpff was told this story long before he had a management role in the hospital setting. The chief of cardiology told him in about 1980 that he had cut his supply budget for the catheterization laboratory by 20% as had been requested. But he said that he had made no other changes in the way the laboratory was operated; so that he would run out of materials by about April 1st or 10 months into the fiscal year. "So they will just have to restore my budget or else have the catheterization lab shut down," the chief commented.

In fact, he may have been asked to deal with an issue for which he was unable to comply effectively, but it was clear that he found the budgeting process a farce, one that did not require any level of adherence or accountability, and he had a plan in mind to force a restoration of the cuts.

The whole situation created an "approach-avoidance mentality." This was only changed when Rapoport, after being appointed as CEO of the newly formed University of Maryland Medical System, said in effect, "it's our problem; we need to own it—and try to fix it."

Toll had recruited Farmer to "clean up the mess" on the UMAB campus, and Farmer recommended privatization and became its champion. The state in effect was saying that the university did not know what it was doing running a hospital and did not know how to run a business. Some in the state government actually suggested that it would be best to take the hospital away from the university and run it as a separate state hospital, something akin to the state mental hospitals. But other states—such as West Virginia, Arizona and Florida—had privatized their university-owned hospitals in the previous few years. Their conversion served as something of a catalyst, and Farmer was able to point to those conversions as examples of an approach. Farmer engaged consultants to help convince the state officials that this was neither a unique or foreign concept. He developed some but not all of his thoughts from his former colleague David R. Challoner, MD, who had been the chancellor at the University of Florida when the Shands Hospital was separated a few years before.

These elements led to the desire and the need to separate the hospital from university governance and state ownership. While some of the needs were clear, the process and results were much less certain. But now 25 years later, the vision of the founders has rung true, and the University of Maryland Medical System has become a major force for high-quality health care in Maryland and the region. It has become a system in the true sense of the word and serves a large portion of the state's population with excellence in care, training for the next generation of health care providers and a venue for clinical research to discover and assess the newest developments in medical care.

LESSONS LEARNED:

As will be emphasized throughout this book, a university hospital needs a strong partnership with its affiliated school of medicine—alignment of agenda, missions, vision for the future and the approaches to achieve those ends. A hospital is an enterprise and needs to be managed as such with innovation, systems, entrepreneurship, and strategic direction. It needs to be free of undue state or university personnel, purchasing protocol and must be able to access the capital markets. A committed, strong and functioning board of directors is essential. Finally, in order to succeed, alignment of vision, mission and strategy must occur with multiple actual and potential partners, such as the state government, the rate-setting commission, the business community and many others. In this case, alignment to state government officials meant accepting accountability for management.

CHAPTER THREE

Process for Achieving Separate Governance—Conception to Birth

No Time to Grieve

At 6:15 a.m., April 10, 1984, my wife awakened me and said, "Nancy Farmer is on the telephone; she is crying."

My wife is a lighter sleeper than I am, and she usually catches the phone on the first ring. She handed me the phone. Nancy was indeed crying, and I heard gasping in the background. She said, "Al is having severe chest pain; please come quickly."

I said, "I'll be there, but call 911 as soon as I hang up."

In less than two minutes I was in my car speeding the three miles from North Roland Park to Hidden Waters, the UMAB chancellor's home on Old Court Road near Greenspring Avenue. By 6:25 a.m. I was climbing the steps to the residence on the second floor to find Farmer gasping on the floor with Nancy crying at his side while holding his hand. He had no pulse and was minimally responsive to my voice. I immediately began chest compression and mouth-to-mouth breathing. Within two to three minutes, the emergency medical services (EMS) team arrived and placed EKG leads while one tech and I continued chest compression and mouth-to-mouth resuscitation.

The EKG recordings showed ventricular fibrillation, and the senior tech said, "Let's try to shock him, but it looks hopeless." Indeed, despite continued resuscitation efforts while we transferred Farmer to Sinai Hospital by ambulance, it was clear that he had died. Subsequent postmortem exam showed a massive acute myocardial infarction. With no time to grieve, at 8:00 a.m. I returned home to shower, shave, dress and go to work as CEO of the University of Maryland Medical System.

What was next? I received a series of phone calls. First, from Clay Mitchell, chairman of the house appropriations committee, calling for Ben Cardin, speaker of the house, and Mickey Steinberg, president of the senate, asking whether we wanted the general assembly to pass the legislation that Farmer had fought for the past two years—that we privatize University Hospital. This was the last day of the session for the general assembly of 1984.

At that point I said, "I'll get back to you."

I called Alan Schwait, soon to be chairman of the University System of Maryland Board of Regents, and Frank Gunther, the chairman designate of the board of the University of Maryland Medical System, the new name for University Hospital should the legislation be enacted. They both asked me the same question: "What do you want to do?"

Suddenly it dawned on me that not only had I lost a close friend but also the man committed to supporting me during a difficult period of transition for the University Hospital. I hesitated and reorganized my thoughts. I imagined that we would be headed for a very, very stressful period in my life. I had no idea what was ahead. I cautiously said, "Let's try it."

How many times would I later think about Farmer, the architect of UMMS privatization, and what might have been had he lived.

-Morton I. Rapoport, MD

Farmer arrived as chancellor of UMAB in the beginning of 1980. By 1982 he had decided how he wished to proceed and named Rapoport, former senior associate dean of the school of medicine, as vice chancellor and chief executive officer of the newly created University of Maryland Medical System.

Rapoport was a Maryland medical school graduate, a U.S. Army veteran of Fort Detrick's biological defense research institute, professor of medicine and former head of medicine at the Baltimore Veterans Administration Hospital. The appointment was not universally hailed; indeed, many department chairs and senior faculty were skeptical at best as to both what UMMS was to be and how Rapoport would handle the new position. At this point UMMS was still within the university; this appointment created a vice chancellor reporting directly to the chancellor rather than a hospital director reporting to the dean of the medical school. Farmer was fond of saying, "We need a person who thinks about the 'bottom line' all the time."

This was his charge to Rapoport. At the time of his appointment, Rapoport commented to Schimpff, "I know there will be blood on the floor. I hope not too much of it will be mine!"

T. Albert Farmer, MD

No one disputed the need for change, but what should be changed and into what form? Farmer, Toll, Dennis, and R Adams Cowley, MD, director of the Maryland Institute for Emergency Medical Services Systems (MIEMSS), all had different and conflicting concepts. In the end Farmer's vision won the day. With the HSCRC characterizing the hospital as high cost and low quality; with the state officials, both the governor and his staff and the legislature, blaming both the hospital and the university for the continued financial deficiencies of the hospital; and the hospital management blaming both the university and the state, it was fundamentally clear that no one wanted to take responsibility for the basic problems. This was a crucial underlying issue—no one wanted to own the problems, preferring to suggest that the problem was caused by others. It should be remembered, however, that hospital leaders whose hands were tied by the burdens of state policies and procedures, were certainly frustrated and legitimately so.

The process for change was difficult. Like other academic institutions, the university had used consultants and committees, but Farmer tried to seek consensus. He sponsored an academic survey to learn what other state institutions had done at the University of Florida, the University of Arizona and the West Virginia University. He also looked to see what had been done across town at Johns Hopkins. Hopkins Hospital and its university—including its medical school—were two separate corporations as set up by the will of Johns Hopkins at his death in the late 1800s. The two corporations had worked effectively together over the years, and Farmer sought to determine if their status as two separate corporations was an impediment or an advantage. Farmer also worked hard to align competing interests and egos. Difficult in any academic institution, this is particularly challenging in a medical environment because control is important, but accountability is often lacking. Essentially, the chancellor led a process over the next two years to craft a proposal to the legislature involving the University System Board of Regents, the medical school leadership and many others. The legislative strategy was complicated, but there were friends and champions within the legislature and the community. A good example was Clarence Mitchell, Jr., often called the "101st Senator" because of his closeness over the years to many in the federal government and his leadership in virtually every national desegregation policy from the 1940s through the 1970s. Mitchell was a member of the university board of regents, and Farmer worked with him and other African Americans with good results. They supported Farmer's vision and, indeed, Mitchell drove to Annapolis with Farmer in a snowstorm to testify for the separate governance legislation. Likewise, because of certain agreements built into the legislation, unions with heavy African-American membership and state employees offered only modest opposition.

Shock Trauma, the clinical arm of MIEMSS, was to be part of UMMS but with certain provisions to maintain some autonomy. This turned out to be a "good break but it did not have to happen that way," observed Rapoport early on.

Shock Trauma had begun as a four-bed unit in University Hospital under the direction of Cowley, an accomplished thoracic surgeon who had seen trauma injuries firsthand in the military and had, through animal studies of trauma, developed the concept of the "golden hour." In brief, his concept showed that a severely traumatized person needed to get to definitive care within an hour; otherwise an irreversible series of metabolic and other changes would begin that would ultimately lead to death. He championed a system that brought trauma patients to a center where a multi-disciplinary team of physicians and nurses provided care, all dedicated solely to trauma patients. He worked with state leaders to establish a communication system and a transport system, including the use of state police helicopters, to bring patients to Shock Trauma within the "golden hour." He was rewarded with excellent outcomes. Cowley worked hard to align the various needed constituencies for the trauma system to work statewide. These included the firefighters, the fire chiefs, the state police, and the legislators. They also included the nine hospitals that were to be part of the system, which agreed that the most serious adult trauma cases would go to Shock Trauma; the children would go to Hopkins, the hand cases to Union Memorial, etc. Each of these hospitals needed to be convinced to "play ball" and commit to this

new system of shared care. Despite his excellent success in bringing all
of these disparate groups together, Cowley was not successful in aligning
Shock Trauma with his own medical school. Alternatively, one could
surmise that since he had developed such a strong alignment between
Shock Trauma and the state government, he may not have felt alignment with the school was either necessary nor even in the best interests
of the center.

Shock Trauma was "different" in its organizational construct from the
rest of the medical school with its departments and divisions. Here was
a multi-disciplinary, cross-departmental and cross-divisional approach
that confounded the status quo and led to arguments about control, resources and, of course, money. The money issue related to the physicians'
practice plan. Cowley had established a practice plan (an organization to
bill and collect for physician care of patients and then to distribute those
dollars to the physicians as their salary) for Shock Trauma rather than
have each physician's parent department (surgery, anesthesiology, etc.)
do its own billing and collecting. Within this Shock Trauma practice
plan, Cowley was able to cross subsidize the anesthesiologists and certain
other specialists who were not able to cover their expenses by using the
collections from the orthopedic surgeons and the general trauma surgeons. Had he followed the usual school practice plan format, it would
have been impossible to do the needed cross subsidization. Further, he
recognized that this was a good way to build teamwork and commitment
among the staff. In 1973, the recently recruited medical school chair of
surgery insisted that Cowley "open the books" to him and indicated that
the dean and chancellor were behind his insistence. Cowley refused and
immediately called Gov. Mandell with whom he had a close relationship. In short order, Mandell visited Shock Trauma and gave the staff as-
surances that their multi-disciplinary approach would be protected. He
then issued an executive order creating a state agency called the Maryland Emergency Medicine Institute (later to become MIEMSS) and
placed it in the Maryland Department of Health and Mental Hygiene
(later to be moved into the university), and he created Shock Trauma
as a separate organization within the university, putting both entities

under the direction of Cowley. Clearly, Cowley had established a strong alignment between Shock Trauma and the state government, especially its governor.

Cowley's Opposition to the Legislation

Farmer came to Baltimore as chancellor of UMAB with a charge to resolve the two leading problems on the campus that held the entire university hostage at the state capitol in Annapolis. Toll, president of the University System of Maryland, and the board of regents were consumed by the sustained conflict between Shock Trauma and the school of medicine that began almost immediately after Cowley was able to create a semi autonomous trauma unit within University Hospital. A series of deans and surgical department chairmen fought with Cowley over issues of accountability and control for many years.

When Farmer arrived in 1980, he was told to resolve the issues surrounding Shock Trauma and the financial failures of the hospital. The hospital was viewed by the HSCRC as one of the most costly hospitals in the state. Furthermore there was serious question about the quality of care being rendered to patients.

Farmer was convinced that he was up to the job. Farmer respected Cowley and assured him that he would work to resolve differences with the medical school leadership in ways that Cowley would find acceptable. Not surprisingly, the dean and the clinical chairmen were not assured nor pleased with Farmer's plan to work with Cowley. Most of the leaders of the school of medicine wanted Cowley out; certainly they did not want to work with him or the clinical staff of Shock Trauma.

Although Farmer did not have an immediate plan to fix the problems in the hospital, he quickly concluded that a study focused on the governance for the hospital was in order. Over a period of nine months, he brought a series of consultants to the campus to help him develop a plan and a strategy to deal with the management deficiencies in the hospital. Farmer, with the consultants' help, developed a plan to separate the hospital from the state and the university. After a search process charged with the responsibility of finding a partner to work with him during a period of transition, Farmer asked me to become CEO of UMMS.

Farmer worked virtually 24/7 to convince the political and university leadership of the wisdom of his plan. The plan was that I would recruit the management team and introduce the processes that would strengthen the hospital, improve the facilities, the quality of care and the financial operations. Farmer assumed the political and legislative strategy himself.

A very vital dimension to the political and legislative strategy was the role of Shock Trauma in the process. Farmer kept Cowley fully briefed and informed as his plan for the hospital emerged. All of the outside consultants recommended that Shock Trauma be included in the new medical system. Indeed the clinical programs of Shock Trauma were a natural part of the hospital operation. On the other hand, the EMS operation had no place in the medical system. Cowley had no interest in dividing the clinical program from the medevac and the pre-hospital services (MIEMSS) which had been carefully designed by him. Furthermore, Cowley had no interest in being accountable to another structure, especially a non-university and a non-state governance system. For some time, Farmer considered keeping Shock Trauma out of the new medical system legislation; he did not want to have Cowley actively undermining his plans in Annapolis.

Farmer and I had many conversations about the governance legislation and the inclusion of Shock Trauma. Although I was convinced of the logic and the benefit to the system by including Shock Trauma as part of the new structure, I was equally convinced that Cowley's opposition and unwillingness to be held accountable to any system would make a difficult job basically impossible.

During the process of developing a coalition in support of legislation, key legislators expressed reservations about the absence of Shock Trauma in the original bill. Indeed some conditioned their support of the bill on whether Shock Trauma was included or not. At this point Farmer concluded that the inclusion of Shock Trauma was not only appropriate but necessary for its passage. Senator Francis X. Kelly, the most important and influential legislator on aspects of Shock Trauma, determined that in a post Cowley era, Shock Trauma would need support and advocacy coming from this new clinical system. Kelly assigned himself the responsibility of writing a bill that would assure Shock Trauma the necessary independence that would preserve and strengthen its mission within the new health care system. Cowley was not assured and certainly not pleased or satisfied. He never spoke to Farmer again and would not speak to Kelly for months after the bill was passed.

-Morton I. Rapoport, MD

The bill was scheduled for a vote on the last day of the legislative session in April 1984. Early that morning Farmer suddenly and unexpectedly died of a heart attack. The legislation nevertheless passed with the formal conversion date set for June 1, 1984. It called for a board of directors to be selected by the governor. Governor Harry R. Hughes, with input from university officials, made those first appointments although from then on governors generally followed recommendations made by the board itself for replacement members. There were a few exceptions. Frank Gunther, first chairman of the board of directors, was not reappointed by the next governor, William Donald Schaefer, because Gunther had been an outspoken advocate for Schaefer's opponent, Stephen Sachs. The board of directors was established with 26 members of which three are to be regents from the university system. The chancellor of the campus (now the president of UMAB), the president of the university (now the chancellor of the University System of Maryland) and the dean of the medical school are members as is the director of MIEMSS, each without vote. The vice president for nursing and the president of the medicine staff organization are ex-officio. There is also a member from the state house of delegates and one from the state senate. All the other members are selected generally by the board itself with recommendation to the governor, but the governor has the final appointment power. The legislation also requires an annual contract between the university and UMMS spelling out such issues as payments to the school of medicine for physician services, rental of facilities from each other and other issues of importance. The legislation also stipulates that the UMMS CEO after selection by the board of directors must be approved by the university system's board of regents and appointed as a vice president of the university. Rapoport always felt that this last requirement was inserted basically as a university strategy to blunt the accountability of the CEO to the UMMS Board of Directors. The regents also had the prerogative to approve any request by UMMS to the state for capital or any plans for entering the bond markets. This was seen as protection to the university which itself had large capital needs and wanted to be certain that the new medical system did not, in effect, become a competitor for state funding.[3]

In retrospect, it is reasonable to question why the legislation creating the separate governance did not also provide funding to deal with the under-capitalized facilities and technology issues. Would it not have been logical to ask for funding for those capital needs at the time the new medical system was created? For example, when similar legislation was passed in West Virginia a few years before, funding was set aside to construct an entirely new hospital building. But in Maryland, the issue at the time was to get the medical system out from state ownership and university governance and to begin the process of institutional accountability. Frankly, few legislative or executive branch leaders would have even considered substantial capital funding at that time. The medical system simply did not have credibility and hence no coalition would have committed to both separation and funding. Alignment with the state government by committing to accountability for institutional success was to be essential for later success, especially when approaching the state for capital dollars for new facilities.

This points out that a real need in the early years after separation was to create credibility. Credibility is like trust; it can be easily lost but takes a long time to gain. The approach used was to begin with the board of directors followed by the HSCRC. With the board made up heavily of Baltimore and Maryland business leaders, credibility could then be extended to the local business community and finally through them to the legislature and the governor's staff. Coincidentally, the increase in credibility within the community allowed the beginnings of

NOTES:

3. Over the years this prerogative of the university and its board of regents was never exercised so long as the university did not feel threatened by the medical system. But once it began to feel threatened in 2007 and 2008, it began to utilize its inherent powers as spelled out in the legislation.

philanthropic activity, which the institution had never had while it was part of the state.

So the basic decision was to proceed with separate governance, work on credibility and borrow, initially, $20 million to make a beginning "dent" in the enormous capital needs of the institution. But Shock Trauma did have statewide credibility and had a coalition in the legislature committed to its success. So the next step in capital development was to get approval from the state for a new building for Shock Trauma. Kelly, a longtime champion of Shock Trauma, was then chair of the senate finance committee. With his leadership and a general legislative sense of support and commitment for the trauma system, the new Shock Trauma building was promptly approved.

LESSONS LEARNED:

Credibility as an adjunct to developing alignment was an essential and critical element of ultimate success. Credibility needed to be developed with the school of medicine, the faculty physicians, the business community, the state government and many others. But credibility, like trust, takes time to develop and requires intense and continuing attention to each party and to their agendas as well as that of the hospital. The death of Farmer, the champion of the new governance and management, who had worked tirelessly for four years to develop credibility, took a major toll on the new medical system's initial development. He had essentially committed to guarantee alignment between the new medical system and the medical school. His commitment to the system's success had been integral to the planning and design; his death, and with it the loss of his commitment and his position of authority within the university, set progress back substantially. Alignment with the school would now take many years to develop. But credibility with the state government could and did begin by accepting its requirement for accountability for institutional success or failure. Over time, gaining alignment with the state government proved to be the medical system's greatest strength, one worth fostering and preserving.

CHAPTER FOUR

Hospital Management Prior to Governance Change—Birth Pains

Steve Ruma Meeting with Al Farmer

Steve Ruma, an organizational development and leadership consultant who had worked with at least 15 leading academic medical centers throughout the country, had a long-term relationship with the University of Maryland that began when Dennis became dean of the medical school. Dennis hired Ruma to help him develop strategies for the department chairmen and for the dean's office. During my years as senior associate dean of the medical school, I developed a trusting and personal relationship with Ruma. When I became CEO of UMMS, I turned to him to help me create a leadership team, a plan, and also to help me develop the transition strategy. I recognized that my success as CEO would depend on my success in developing a collaborative relationship with the dean and president. Trust would be essential because the change process and the accountability process would create tension, hopefully creative tension, within the system. Ruma cautioned me not to be too aggressive, not to go too fast and not to be too optimistic about the process. He was not certain that all of the parties would agree that alignment was important from their perspective. He reminded me of the quote in The Prince:

> "It should be borne in mind that there is nothing more difficult to manage or more doubtful of success or more dangerous to handle than to take the lead in introducing a new order of things. For the innovator has enemies in all those who are doing well under the old order, and he has only lukewarm defenders in all those who would benefit under the new order."

Ruma and I agreed that we needed to test Dennis and Farmer on their willingness to develop a collaborative strategy with me as we began to develop

*an entrepreneurial vision for the medical system. A meeting was set up with
Farmer, Dennis and his new associate dean, Marjorie Wilson, MD. Wilson
was appointed to the position that I vacated, and she was not pleased that I was
in charge of the hospital. She hoped to become dean of the medical school and
did not support the separation of the hospital from the state and from the medical school. She believed that she was quite capable of running the hospital and
the medical school as well. Ironically she had worked with Ruma for more than
10 years while she was vice president at the Association of American Medical
Colleges (AAMC).*

*The meeting with Farmer, Dennis, Wilson, Rapoport and Ruma did not
go well. Not surprisingly, Dennis and Wilson had no interest in supporting me
or assisting in a transition strategy for the hospital. What was very surprising
was that Farmer had no interest as well; his view was that the inevitable stress
and conflict that would arise from change would be arbitrated by him; he would
be the "integrator." Privately after the meeting he assured me that he would
be my advocate and my friend. Both Ruma and I were not assured. Farmer's
death six months later demonstrated how vulnerable systems and organizations
can be when strategies and processes are dependent on single individuals and
lack broad-based support.*

*The absence of consensus and agreement at the outset doomed the organi-
zation and its leaders to a long period of tension and conflict.*

-Morton I. Rapoport, MD

For many years there had been no effective accountability at University Hospital. Indeed, most involved tended to point to structural problems or to other agencies for the problems within. Accountability was
sorely needed.

Rapoport was named chief executive officer of the new medical system in 1982 while it was still part of the university. The next two years
were spent preparing for the governance change that was expected to
occur. Most of the issues related to finances. It was a time for budget
development and monitoring at a level never before done within University Hospital. The accounting system needed to be switched from the
cash accounting system used by state agencies to an accrual accounting
system used by most businesses and required by the HSCRC method-

ologies. The medical system had no capacity to be accountable to the HSCRC initially. It could not comply with the regulations that standard reports be submitted in a timely manner. It simply did not have the systems in place to produce these required reports. It was also a time to develop systems for approvals, hiring, purchasing and other basic services. The beginnings of credibility occurred when the operating margin swung from negative $4.5 million to positive $6.6 million on operating revenue of $163 million. As the accounting systems improved, another issue began to be apparent. The pension costs in the state system were high, and the HSCRC indicated that it would not put that level of costs into the hospital rate structure. The commission believed it was not justifiable to pass these costs on to those who paid the hospital bills, namely the insurers and patients.

In effect, the commission said, "Go back to the state and ask them to cover those excess costs." This became known within the medical system as the "pension gap," and will be discussed in more detail later.

Among the initial management team members that Rapoport inherited was Robert Ginn, the chief financial officer. A very intelligent individual, he was described by longtime CFO and current CEO Robert Chrencik "as being like a fireman who poured water on the blazing fire and brought it under control."

Ginn conceptualized that the medical system needed a unique rate structure with the HSCRC. Other hospitals all had a single rate structure for their hospital but Ginn requested separate rates for University Hospital, Shock Trauma and the cancer center on the basis that the latter two were inherently different and therefore needed to have their cost structures analyzed separately by the commission. This made a huge impact since Shock Trauma and the cancer center got higher rates than would have been possible with an all-encompassing rate for the entire medical system. This was the first step towards financial viability which in turn was followed by much better billing and collections. It was also Rapoport's first "lesson" in the use of alignment.

Meanwhile, Chrencik was a consultant to the university and medical system developing the relationship with the HSCRC. He, Rapoport and Farmer developed a non-adversarial relationship, much different than the approach that had been taken in the past and, indeed, that had been taken and is taken today by many of the hospitals around state. In effect they asked the HSCRC to "give us some time while we improve the systems."

Shortly, the medical system began filing reports that were complete and on time. In effect the medical system basically agreed to be accountable to the commission, and the commissioners responded in kind by giving the medical system time to make the corrections needed and to develop a functional relationship rather than an adversarial one.

So over time, the medical system slowly became accountable to the commission, to the state, to the hospital committee of the board of regents and to others. In effect, the medical system was developing alignment with the state government by accepting the responsibility to be accountable for its own operations and finances and with the commission by accepting and responding to their requirements. This would prove to be exceptionally valuable in the years to come. All of this set up a positive situation for the medical system to emerge as a separate, not-for-profit corporation in June 1984.

LESSONS LEARNED:
Developing accountability to various stakeholders, such as the governor, the legislature and HSCRC, was a critical element in establishing credibility. The state would later reciprocate with capital funding as will be described later. The new approach of interacting with the commission as a partner, which merited respect and responsiveness, allowed for a successful request to have separate rates for University Hospital, Shock Trauma and the cancer center. These in turn were critical to the early financial successes of the new medical system. The concept of alignment was beginning.

CHAPTER FIVE

The First Years—Infancy

Cowley Invites Rapoport to Take a Helicopter Ride

In late 1985, Maryland experienced its second major tragedy in the medevac program in a period of five years when two troopers and a patient were killed in a crash outside Baltimore. What made this tragedy even worse was that the crash was not located for more than three hours after it was reported missing. Maryland is a small populous state; it was hard to imagine how a crash could occur and not be located for such a long time.

It was determined that the entire helicopter fleet lacked bad weather systems and communication capacity that was considered state of the art. Stated another way, the helicopter fleet needed to be replaced in its entirety. The state police, the general assembly and the governor responded to public opinion. All agreed that the medevac system was the state's pride and joy, and the medevac fleet needed to be replaced.

The legislature and the governor were in agreement that an urgent process needed to be implemented to purchase eight new helicopters rapidly; the challenge was how to pay for them. Despite a promise of no new taxes, it was agreed that the state would introduce a motor vehicle fee that would fund a plan to purchase the new helicopters and support their maintenance, as well as fund other critical elements of the state's evolving EMS system.

A highly competitive bidding and selection process was developed with the objective of selecting a new helicopter that would have state of the art communications systems and bad weather capability. Maryland was seen as the leader of a nationwide trend to increased use of helicopters for medevac and inter-hospital transport of patients. The selection of a vendor by the State of Maryland would provide great prestige in a very competitive industry. The state police and the governor looked to Cowley as a key participant in the selection process.

Although UMMS and Shock Trauma would benefit greatly by the state's expanded and more advanced medevac capacity, I and my management team were only interested bystanders to the selection process and the politics.

The timing of the vendor selection was shortly before the time that the clinical chiefs had gone public to demand my removal as CEO. One afternoon in September, Cowley called to tell me that the CEO of Aerospatiale, a French manufacturer of helicopters was on campus and wanted to see me. Cowley was most anxious for the state to select Aerospatiale. He asked me if I would take a ride in the helicopter. For a fleeting moment, perhaps an insane moment, I thought that the clinical chiefs had come up with an ingenious plan to remove me. I would be killed in a helicopter crash. (It is often said: "It is not paranoia if they really are against you.")

My immediate response to Cowley was that I would only take the ride if he was on the helicopter with me. At the time I did not realize the Aerospatiale pilot would let Cowley pilot the craft for some of the time in the air. For more than an hour in a helicopter high over Baltimore and it suburbs I had the most exciting yet the most scary period in my life.

-Morton I. Rapoport, MD

A corporate enterprise depends upon the collective wisdom of its board of directors. UMMS was blessed to have superb individuals appointed by the governor, individuals who gave unstintingly of their time and energy. But the separate governance legislation had some built in pitfalls and ambiguities which soon created a new set of problems to resolve.

The enactment of the legislation created an immediate need for a board of directors for the newly independent hospital. A critical first question was who would chair the board. In Florida, when a similar governance arrangement was devised a few years before, the chairman of the board of the new hospital corporation was the university chancellor.

But after some discussion, Farmer agreed that it would be best to have an external individual serve as chair; so that all members of the new board could aspire to the position of chair and as a result all work harder over the course of their terms. Others in the university opposed this approach; some did so quietly whereas some did so actively. In essence, these individuals wanted the university to maintain its control over the hospital and not cede it to an outside group. Having the chancellor as chair would maintain some semblance of control. Privately, Farmer in all likelihood would have liked to have chaired the board as he thought it would have been consistent with his position as chancellor, and since he was personally so committed to seeing the new enterprise succeed. On the other hand, he appreciated the importance of having a vital and viable board of directors and hence understood the need for the outside chair. It is also likely that he recognized the university leadership **at** the time did not share his enthusiasm for hospital independence.

The legislation stipulated that the chancellor of the UMAB campus (Farmer), the president of the University System of Maryland (Toll), the dean of the medical school (Dennis) and the director of MIEMSS (Cowley) would all be members of the board, ex-officio and without vote. The medical school dean essentially saw this situation as an affront. To Dennis and his colleagues the issue was a lack of authority. (Some years later the board voted to ask the legislature to change the law, giving these individuals a vote. However the then-chairman of the university's board of regents, Peter O'Malley, asked that the request not be brought to the legislature at that time because it would interfere potentially with other issues that he was bringing forward. Since then the issue has remained moot, and deans and others have recognized that if they demonstrate their credibility to the board, any reasonable request would be honored. Specifically, once a dean had developed credibility with the board, if he or she spoke against a plan that was being proposed, that request would almost undoubtedly carry the day with the board.) At the time, however, the lack of vote for these individuals created tension, and that tension would lead to open conflict some years later, as will be discussed below.

Prior to the governance separation, the regents had created a "hospital" committee to oversee issues of University Hospital. It was chaired by Schwait, a prominent Baltimore lawyer and later a Baltimore judge and soon-to-be regents chair. The committee included not only regents but external community members including Gunther. The chair of the regents suggested Gunther as not only a board member of the new UMMS but also as the initial chair At that time Gunther was well positioned with Mayor Schaefer and Gov. Hughes. He had been tapped over the years for major volunteer positions, such as leading the United Way, leading the fund raising for the new National Aquarium in downtown Baltimore at the inner harbor and major activities within the Catholic Archdiocese. Gunther had the ability not to get caught up in a "million dramas" but instead maintained the vision to seek the public interest in all he did. The governor also picked local business people, such as Richard Hug, CEO of Environmental Elements, George McGowan, COO and later CEO of Baltimore Gas and Electric, Henry Butta, vice president and CEO of Chesapeake and Potomac Telephone Company, and Alvin Wolpoff, CEO of Wolpoff and Company to join the board. Others included Patricia Smyth, a well-known civic activist who later became chair of the Medstar board; Marion Pines, advisor to the mayor; Shirley Phillips, co-founder of Phillips Seafood; Edmund Fick, banker; Joseph Hardiman, soon to be leader of NASD; John Webb, lawyer; and

Signing the separate governance legislation, front row: Senate President Melvin Steinberg, Governor Harry Hughes and Speaker Benjamin Cardin.

Thomas Hutchison, developer. The board composition was unique in that it included the corporate members but also community activists like Catherine Borne, a professor at Maryland's school of social work and a community activist in the West Baltimore area. The board included a number of African-American community leaders, among them Uthman Ray, MD; Lisa Williams, MSW; Larry Young, state house delegate; Akneil Muldrow, CEO of Development Credit Fund; and, later, George Russell, lawyer, city solicitor and one-time candidate for mayor. By statute the board included a member each from the house of delegates and the senate; the first members were Del. Young and Sen. Kelly.

The board found that it was involved in a learning opportunity. The diverse group shared a common goal of making a "sick" hospital become "well" again. The time commitment of each board member was prodigious and that of the chair, and later chairs, was truly monumental.

One of the key steps for the new board of directors was to develop a strong working relationship with the university's board of regents. Since the board of directors of UMMS had three members who were regents, they became the conduit for most interactions between the regents and the board. At the same time there were ongoing interactions between the CEO of the medical system with the administration of the medical school, the Baltimore campus and the overall university system. One of the prerogatives of the board of regents was to approve an annual contract, and the three regents became a de facto committee of the regents to make the necessary recommendations to the parent board of regents. As a practical matter, whenever issues arose between the university and the medical system, such as the amount of funding to put into the physician services contract, the three regent members along with three non-regent members of the board of directors would meet to work out any necessary compromises. Usually the two boards would accept the negotiated settlement.

By law, the UMMS board of directors was made up entirely of Maryland residents. It seemed to Rapoport and also to Farmer that it would be advantageous to create a national advisory board whose purpose would be to serve as a sort of kitchen cabinet of "wise men" who understood university, medical school and university hospital issues, governance constraints and were strong at both strategy and tactics. Three individuals were chosen for this purpose including David M. Bray, executive dean of Harvard Medical School; Challoner, by then chancellor of St. Louis University; and Saul Farber, MD, dean of the New York University School of Medicine. These three would meet on an intermittent basis but were available for phone consultation at all times and proved to be particularly useful in the first three to four years of the new organization.

Mort Rapoport—Successful Because He was Persistent

In 1969, I was appointed to the National Cancer Institute's Baltimore Cancer Research Center located at the Public Health Service Hospital in Baltimore. Asked to develop a research and clinical program around infections in patients with advanced cancer, I requested assistance since I had only just finished my internal medicine residency and there was no one at the BCRC with that type of expertise. Shortly, I had two mentors— Richard Hornick, MD, head of infectious diseases at the University of Maryland School of Medicine, and Mort, then professor in the division. They alternated weeks coming to the BCRC to review cases with me and to offer instruction and guidance. It was an exciting time for me, and they also seemed to enjoy the opportunity to see a different type of patient than usual, ours being mostly those with acute leukemia receiving aggressive cancer chemotherapy. When one of them was busy, they would send a colleague, Frank M. Calia, MD, who would later become, among other roles, chief of medicine at the veterans hospital, vice dean and chairman of the department of medicine. Hornick later became chair of medicine in Rochester, and Mort became first chief of medicine at the veterans hospital, then senior associate dean and then CEO of the medical system. The learning experience for me was outstanding, and it certainly had a major impact on my career. I had planned to remain at the center for two years and then move on. But Mort recognized that I was enjoying the work and had published some papers. Maybe this was my calling and why didn't I think about some laboratory training at the National Institute of Allergy and Infectious Diseases. Although he was persistent in wanting me to stay on, it was good advice and I spent a year in Bethesda learning immunology related to fungal infections. By the time I returned to Baltimore, Mort was chief of medicine at the veterans hospital. We maintained our friendship, usually over a corned beef sandwich at lunch. Some years later we were having just such a lunch at Lexington Market when he told me that he felt somewhat over extended in his role as CEO of the new medical system.

"I think I should create a new position to help me out; what do you think?" he asked.

So we talked about it and I went back to my job as director of the cancer center. About two weeks later he called and asked me to stop by. My wife and I were leaving the next morning on a week's trip, and her mother was coming to watch over our daughter.

"Sorry, but I am just leaving to go to the airport to pick up my mother-in-law," I replied.

But Mort was persistent. "Just stop by for a minute or two."

So I did as requested.

When I arrived he said, "Remember our conversation? I have talked to the university chancellor, to the medical system board chair and to the board chair of the regents—they all agree that you should become executive vice president of the medical system. Will you accept?"

I remembered our conversation but never thought he was thinking about me, and I certainly had not thought about the job after that lunch. So all I could think of to say was, "I need to go to the airport and pick up my mother-in-law."

We agreed that I would think about the position, and we would talk when I got back to town in a week. So instead of lying on the beach with nothing important to think about, my wife and I spent a lot of time discussing this opportunity.

When we did get back home Saturday evening, the first thing my mother-in-law said was, "There is a Dr. Rapoport that called twice this afternoon, and he wants you to call him as soon as you come in."

It was at that moment that I learned that Mort can be very persistent!

The next day we met at his home and drew up a job description. I started
two weeks later.

-Stephen C. Schimpff, MD

With help from these three individuals, Rapoport began selecting a
management team. As in many such organizational situations, some of
the initial members of the team proved not to be perfect fits and moved
on to other endeavors. But over time a core management team evolved
which persisted, with some comings and goings, throughout the next
23 years. These included Schimpff as executive vice president and chief
operating officer and later the medical center's chief executive officer.
Schimpff was the director of the cancer center, a professor of medicine
and had worked for the NCI for 13 years prior to joining the university
in 1982. Others included Chrencik, initially as a consultant (Peat Mar-
wick) and later as budget director and then as chief financial officer;
John Ashworth, longtime executive director of both Shock Trauma and
MIEMSS, initially as vice president for strategic planning and business
development and later medical center chief operating officer and then
chief executive officer; Sharon O'Keefe, RN, MS; followed by Katherine
McCullough, RN, MS, as senior vice president for patient care services
and operations; and M. Nicholas Humphries as chief counsel. Nelson Sabatini joined the management team after completing his term as Maryland Secretary of Health and Mental Hygiene for Gov. Schaefer, and
Mark Wasserman joined after having been chief of staff and then secretary of business and economic development to Gov. Schaefer. Alison
Brown, RN, MPH, and Henry Franey, MBA, joined in the early 1990s to
lead business development and planning and finance, respectively.

Steve Schimpff—"Moses had His Brother, Aaron"

Perhaps I owe Steve Schimpff my greatest gratitude and appreciation for
our achievements and success over almost 40 years. Our first meeting
occurred when Steve was a young clinical investigator at the NCI's Bal-
timore Cancer Research Center. The BCRC was located in the public
health hospital adjacent to the Johns Hopkins undergraduate campus in
Wyman Park. Steve invited me to work with him as a consultant in in-

fectious diseases between 1969 and 1972. It was exciting for me to visit BCRC monthly to consult with Steve on problem patients with infection at the BCRC. I recognized Steve's creativity and his collaborative skills. In fact those collaborative skills have characterized Steve in virtually every initiative that he has undertaken to this day. He grew as a clinician and as an academic investigator over the years at BCRC and later at the University of Maryland. The BCRC moved to the University of Maryland campus in 1974 and in 1982 it was transformed into the University of Maryland Cancer Center. Steve became the director; during his period of leadership the cancer center grew in size, in recognition and success. Steve was respected throughout the nation as a leader who championed interdisciplinary care in the treatment of cancer. Steve and I frequently shared our passion for interdisciplinary and multispecialty care as a coming frontier for American medicine. Our shared view was that the University of Maryland was far ahead of most hospitals in the nation with the growth and success of Shock Trauma and now the cancer center. Both of these programs had their detractors in the school of medicine since most of the clinical chairmen saw interdisciplinary activities as threats to their autonomy and the control that clinical chairmen normally exert. But Steve and I were comfortable with the knowledge that pioneers are rarely greeted with universal support.

Our struggle and Steve's efforts to craft the cancer center vision met a serious roadblock when John Kastor, MD, was made chairman of medicine and received assurance from the dean of the school of medicine (Dennis) that the cancer center would be essentially "merged" into the department of medicine. Indeed a similar agreement between the chairman of surgery and the dean was reached for Shock Trauma. Never mind that the dean did not have the authority to negotiate these agreements.

With the creation of UMMS, Shock Trauma and the cancer center became two of the most visible centers of excellence within the medical system. For me personally they were programs that I believed could serve to distinguish the hospital as a national leader. Unfortunately the vision that Steve and I shared was not held by many. We shared this vision with Farmer on many occasions. He concurred that it was worth striving for and was supportive.

During Steve's directorship of the cancer center, he and I had numerous conversations in an effort to strengthen the independence of the cancer center despite the alternative attempts by others. We recognized that the short term survival of the medical system was essential to the long term survival of the cancer center and Shock Trauma. It was at this point in 1985 that I proposed to Steve that he join me as executive vice president of the medical system; I needed help. Together we managed the many, many challenges that would bring UMMS the success that we achieved by the time that we both retired.

I often think about the statement that one of our board members, Sen. Kelly, who was a great fan of Bible studies, made to me: "You know Mort, Moses had his Aaron; don't you think Steve is like Aaron?"

-Morton I. Rapoport, MD

Creating operating systems was a major challenge. Most institutions take operating systems for granted. One just assumes that effective systems are in place, but they simply did not exist at the University Hospital between 1982 and 1984. They had to be introduced as enterprise systems to replace the current state systems of management. There was nothing wrong with the state systems except that they did not fit the requirements of a private not-for-profit corporation answerable to the rate-setting commission, the board of directors and others. So the process for change was intense yet required patience. It was as much as anything a culture change, and any culture change takes time. Yet the processes needed to be rapid if the new medical system was to be successful. These two conflicting sides of the same issue made for difficult management. Culture change was a major issue for the new management team. The hospital was full of good and well-intended individuals who had never before worked in an enterprise environment. The issue then was to transform them and the systems at the same time in a way that was effective yet appropriate. One culture change was a relentless focus on finances. This focus was effective over time, and yet it delayed an adequate focus on quality and other important issues facing an academic medical center. The collective wisdom, strongly emphasized by board member Richard

Hug, was "no money, no mission." So finances had to be the first and foremost focus or else other critical issues could never be developed. Indeed the financial issues along with the facility and technology inadequacies were frankly overwhelming at that time. The result was that some, such as the director of quality management, felt frustrated that senior management would not give quality more attention. Interestingly enough, the school of medicine never really helped deal with quality and safety issues. The school leadership was content to leave this to the medical system leadership. They never opposed but never materially assisted. An exception was when an issue related to a series of malpractice cases developed in the department of surgery that affected both school and medical system. This led to the implementation of an outside review process and brought on necessary changes in management.

The state budget by its very nature is not entrepreneurial, and the state accounting system is a cash accounting system, not an accrual accounting system as used by business. This budgeting and accounting process influenced the hospital and the university staff in what they did. However the HSCRC required an accrual accounting system and an independent outside audit. One of the first agenda items in creating a new finance department was a new approach to budgeting and accounting. It was also necessary to create departments for functions previously handled by the university, such as payroll, information systems, telecommunications, facilities, housekeeping, and dietary. The decision was made by Rapoport to purchase some services from the university for a number of years. These included personnel, purchasing and security. Since so many of the employees, although paid by the new medical system, were still state employees it made sense to have personnel functions remain with the university. Similarly the university had a good purchasing system and capable department; so it was deemed wise to maintain that function with the university. The same was true for security. During a span of about three years, however, new departments within the medical system assumed all of these functions.

But a number of issues not dealt with in the legislation began to be problematic. One was the problem of having what was in effect a "dual personnel system." Those who had been state employees were able to retain state employment benefits, such as the retirement system, many holidays, and the like, including having raises set by government mandate. New hires in the medical system, however, became part of the system's personnel structure, with fewer holidays, a different retirement system that was a defined contribution rather than a defined benefit plan, and salary increases based on merit. The legislature had assumed that there would be a fairly rapid turnover of employees over a few years such that this issue did not need to be dealt with in advance. An incident in 1986 made the problem overt. That year Christmas fell on a Thursday, and Gov. Hughes decided to give all state employees Friday as an added holiday. This meant that the medical system, which as a hospital requires staff present 24 hours per day, seven days a week, had to pay individuals double time for working that Friday, an expense that totaled about $400,000. Rapoport analogized that this was equivalent to the governor "writing a check on the medical system's bank account without concurrently making a deposit."

The pension issue was also significant. The HSCRC said that the state pension provisions were simply far and away too costly compared to every other hospital in the state, and there was no reason why that added expense should be covered in the rate structure. The medical system was told to go back to the state and ask for the differential. Eventually Rapoport and Chrencik went to Gov. Schaefer and asked for help.

A meeting in late December that included Charles Benton, his secretary of the budget, led the governor to say: "I'm not Santa Claus," and he then turned to Benton and said, "Charlie, tell them I'm not Santa Claus."

Nevertheless, he agreed to a program that would encourage the former state employees to convert to the medical system employment ranks by both promising to have them remain in the state pension plan and giving individuals a one-time bonus payment for converting to medical system employment. With only a few exceptions, most employees made the conversion. This effectively resolved the pension gap issue and the dual personnel system.

A second issue that arose as a result of the way in which the legislation had been created had to do with the governance of Shock Trauma. The center had been initiated by Cowley, also a professor of surgery within the school of medicine. The initial center was a four-bed unit on the fourth floor of the south hospital building. By the time the medical system was created in 1984, it had grown to about 40 beds. In addition, the visionary Cowley had created an overall system within the state of Maryland to deal with anyone who sustained trauma. The overarching institution, MIEMSS, is generally regarded as the best in the country, the traumatized individual is taken by ambulance or by helicopter to the appropriate location based upon the degree of injury. This might be the local hospital emergency room for a relatively minor injury, a regional trauma center for more serious injury or Shock Trauma for those who have sustained head, spinal cord or multisystem injuries. Such adults are taken to Shock Trauma whereas seriously injured children are taken to Johns Hopkins Hospital and those with extensive burns are admitted to the burn center at Johns Hopkins Bayview. The system has worked well for many years, and the survival results are indeed impressive.

With the new governance arrangement, Shock Trauma was part of UMMS but the rest of MIEMSS was a part of the university. The governance mechanism was complicated, intentionally, to maintain a level of autonomy for Shock Trauma along with MIEMSS. But this raised the question: was Shock Trauma a true part of UMMS or not really? Tensions began to rise because these issues had not been resolved when the legislation was written, and there was a significant added complication in that the medical school, like all medical schools, was organized around disciplines such as medicine, surgery, pediatrics, etc. But Shock Trauma was organized around a medical problem—trauma—a disease orientation. A trauma center just did not fit the medical school formula because it included surgeons, internists, anesthesiologists, and others all focused on a single disease. This raised the classic "disease vs. discipline" controversy common in many medical schools, often related to the creation and development of a cancer center. So at least three different forces were at work. One was the medical system's attempt to organize

itself and manage its parts. A second was Cowley and MIEMSS trying
to hold its parts together in an autonomous manner. Third was Shock
Trauma's "difference" from the medical school approach with its disease
orientation and hence its structure, organization, practice plan and culture. This was essentially anathema to the school of medicine.

These early issues not adequately dealt with in the legislation were
now proving problematic—the pension gap/dual personnel system, the
Shock Trauma governance, and the lack of a vote on the board by the
dean of the medical school, the campus chancellor and president of the
university. These three issues, each a result of the legislative process,
began to extract substantial time and energy from the leadership of the
medical system and, quite frankly, led to tensions, controversy and difficulties in management.

One of the important early endeavors of the new medical system
leadership was to begin a process of improving the facilities and upgrad-
ing the technology. Chrencik developed data to show that a truly huge
capital infusion would be needed to rebuild the facilities. He brought in
Kaufmann-Hall, a healthcare financial consulting firm, for advice, and
they in turn assisted in creating an engagement with First Chicago Bank
and Trust. The First Chicago individuals felt that the medical system
had promise and a good management team, and they felt that the leadership presented credible plans. They therefore initiated a line of credit
for facility upgrades of $20 million which later was to rise to $27 million.
This allowed the most basic renovations to start, particularly in the older
south hospital building which was built in 1933. The improvements included infrastructure upgrades such as air conditioning, which did not
exist in the south hospital at that time, the construction of shafts to
carry the new air conditioning ductwork plus electrical and plumbing
conduits, basic improvements to the roof and the like. Funds were also
used to do floor by floor renovations of the south hospital, which cost
about $1 million per wing. With four wings on each of 13 floors, the
$20–27 million would never be enough to finish the job and do much-
needed work in the newer (1972) north hospital building as well. An
upgrade meant completely demolishing a wing back to bare brick walls

and then restarting with new electrical, new plumbing and first-time air conditioning and then rebuilding the necessary interior walls and ceiling along with appropriate lighting—highly expensive even in 1980s' dollars.

Rapoport, Cowley, Sen. Kelly and other key board members approached the governor and the legislature for funding of a new $47 million building for Shock Trauma Center. This was granted, and the new building opened in 1989. At the time of the certificate of need development, the plan was for 72 critical care beds and 66 intermediate care beds. As the planning process proceeded and the funding became clearer, it was necessary to remove two floors from the building and place the intermediate care beds within adjacent hospital areas on the fourth floor of the south building. Cowley was livid at the change, but it went ahead by necessity. He tried to have Shock Trauma relocated to the Mt. Wilson Hospital site (built in the 1930s for tuberculosis patients and by the late 1980s was ready for closure). Basically he received no support from the legislature, and construction on the downtown campus proceeded. In short, the Mt. Wilson site made no sense since Shock Trauma would and did need the adjacency of other medical services such as cardiac surgery and thoracic surgery plus all of the support services that would not be possible at Mt. Wilson. But Cowley was most displeased and never moved into the office built for him in the new building after it opened.

R Adams Cowley and John Ashworth

The golden hour and vision of Shock Trauma has been rightly credited to Cowley, a man for the ages, and a man that I was privileged to call my friend. Without question the person that deserves credit for helping to execute the vision was Ashworth who would later assume a major leadership role in the medical system. Early in the development of Shock Trauma, Cowley hired a young hospital administrator with organizational and management skills that complemented Cowley. Ashworth's military background of MASH units in Vietnam appealed to Cowley but more importantly Ashworth shared Cowley's passion and perhaps most importantly his loyalty, and the vision was total. Over his years as Cowley's deputy,

Ashworth crafted the pre-hospital system, the physician practice plan and the relationships with university and state agencies. In fact, Ashworth was involved in virtually every aspect of MIEMSS and Shock Trauma operations. In the year prior to the legislation separating the hospital from the state and the university I met with Farmer and said we must approach the state for a separation gift. We need to ask for support for a new center because the hospital will not have the capital capacity to build and expand Shock Trauma. Farmer concurred, and I turned to Ashworth and said, "begin the planning process, we will get the support."

By 1989 the R A. Cowley Trauma Center was dedicated. It was and is the finest and largest trauma center in the country. Cowley never said thank you to Ashworth or Sen. Kelly, the two people that did the most in making the new building happen. He simply said the building was too small. He then said to me, "It's just another example of your lean-to and shanty vision."

-Morton I. Rapoport, MD

Rapoport would later present to the governor and the legislature the concept of a public-private partnership in which the state had provided the $47 million for Shock Trauma, and the medical system—through debt, philanthropy and retained net income—had provided nearly $75 million, a substantially larger share for other renovations of the medical center. The basic concept was that UMMS, in effect, had broken away from the state, but it was grossly undercapitalized at the time. As the second board chairman, Roger Lipitz, would say: "the state gave us a negative asset when it formed the new corporation."

So UMMS needed to go back to the state and claim, appropriately, that it was the location for much of the teaching by the medical school faculty of both medical students and residents. These individuals needed a decent place to teach if the school was ever to reach its full potential. Although it sounded counter intuitive to go back to the state and ask for funding for facility upgrades, it was in fact a necessity to ultimate success.

A Little Advice From a Friend

With the emphasis on hospital length of stay and utilization review begin-ning in the late 1970s, hospital managers and physicians began to seriously examine their respective roles in improving efficiency and productivity in clinical care. Insurance companies and state and federal programs seri-ously began strategies to compare hospitals, individual physicians and re-gions of the country looking at frequency of procedures, hospital length of stay, utilization of ancillary services including radiology, laboratory and pharmacy.

It was in this context that I was approached by one of my close friends and former college roommate in 1985. Herbert Kushner, MD, was head of the general medicine division of the department of medicine. He and I were high school friends and college roommates at Franklin and Marshall College from 1955 to 1956. He entered Johns Hopkins Medical School in 1956, and I entered the University of Maryland School of Medicine at the same time. We maintained our friendship over the years that followed, and he joined the University of Maryland faculty in the late 1970s. On more than one occasion while I was senior associate dean of the school of medicine and later as CEO of UMMS, Herb made observations and sug-gestions about how I could do my job better.

In late 1985, he saw me walking through the hospital and said, "I think I have an explanation about why our length of stay in many cases exceeds Johns Hopkins. The elevators stink; we don't have enough; they are frequently out of order and no one seems to care."

He was right, except that I cared and was frustrated. The south hos-pital elevators were old, repair parts were hard to come by, and a program to replace the elevators with new ones was delayed because of insufficient capital. The north hospital was opened in the early 1970s after the state built that addition while meeting a budget shortfall by removing multiple elevators from the plan. Indeed the psychiatry building elevators which were also in disrepair were used to supplement the south hospital deficien-cies. Kushner's point was that patients arrived two to three hours late for surgical procedures and radiologic or diagnostic procedures because they were waiting for elevators. As a result cases were frequently cancelled and rescheduled because patients arrived too late. Perhaps other hospitals had similar problems, but my assumption was that ours were worse.

Beginning with completion of the new building for Shock Trauma in 1989 and every new one thereafter we planned to have additional elevators to provide redundancies for the "under elevatored" older hospital buildings. Finally, over time, the problem was resolved as new buildings with extra elevators were added. The lesson of course is that elevators were important, and that scrimping on them during the building process created serious and lasting consequences. My frustration was that we could not afford to fix them or add more for many years.

-Morton I. Rapoport, MD

Another area of concern was the emergency room. Like most academic medical centers, the emergency room in the early 1980s was run largely by the resident staff. A national report had been offered noting that most academic medical centers did not have adequate supervision of the care of patients, especially those coming to the emergency room. Since the passage of the Medicare and Medicaid laws by the U.S. Congress in the 1960s, it was illegal to have two classes of care; now everyone was a private patient. Seeking the best possible way to address this issue, Rapoport visited Georgetown University Hospital's ER and met with its director, Michael Rolnick, MD. He asked Rolnick to visit Baltimore and do a consult. Rolnick recommended that UMMS begin a program with faculty on site and directing the ER. He suggested one of his senior residents, Robert Barish, MD, for the job. Barish was selected and became the youngest ER director of an academic medical center in the country. He in turn recruited Brian Browne, MD, and Elizabeth Tso, MD, as an initial team of attendings to revamp the way the emergency department worked. They began July 1, 1985, and emergency medicine was created as a separate clinical service within UMMS with Barish as the physician-in-chief.

The residents were concerned. Would this mean that they would no longer have the opportunity to learn by doing? Harry Oken, MD, today a highly regarded general internist in Columbia, Md., was a resident in the emergency department when the new regime began. He was upset that the new approach in the emergency room would hinder the resident's work and reduce the opportunity for learning. Oken shortly realized, however—as he told us many years later—that residents learned much more from the attendings and their teaching. But in addition, the new team also watched over patients in a more careful manner. The result was an increased quality of care and an increased quality of education. Indeed, over time, the emergency room became a favorite elective for students in the medical school. Despite its popularity, department status was not granted to emergency medicine until 2007. But it did have its own practice plan and was highly successful.

Barish, followed by Browne, grew the emergency medical department both in excellence and in volumes. Their first priority was clinical excellence followed by educational excellence. Within a short period of time, they had developed the country's largest emergency medicine residency program; quite a feat given that the residency had been disbanded immediately before their arrival.

Given the developing reputation for quality care, over time they were invited to take over the management of the emergency rooms at Mercy Medical Center in downtown Baltimore, then the Veterans Administration Hospital across the street, then Bon Secours Hospital a few blocks away. In each of these settings full-time faculty were placed at the other hospital's ER with the expectation that they would rotate back one day per week but be fully paid by the other hospital. This allowed Barish to gain more staff without added UMMS funding. After Barish became first head of Maryland Medicine and then associate dean for clinical affairs, Browne assumed the directorship. Under his leadership, they were invited to take over the ER in Hagerstown, Md., then the two ERs at the Shore Health System on the eastern shore of Maryland and then the two ERs in the Upper Chesapeake Health System in Harford County to the northeast. These hospitals, at greater distance from the medical center, were developed using a non-full-time faculty approach but all had voluntary appointments in the medical school. Clearly the approach that Barish, Browne and their colleagues had put into place had been highly successful. Further, these "outposts" were responsible for directing more than 500 referrals per year to the medical center and the faculty specialists.

Bob Chrencik

One morning about 8:30 a.m., Bob came into my office with a cup of coffee in his hand and said, "We need to talk."

I could tell he was serious. He sat down and began, "Net income has been off for the past two months, and now I need to tell you that it will be down again this month. We need to act, now."

Bob, I already well knew, was very strategic in his thinking and also had a good sense of what to do in a tactical way as well.

"We can and should work on costs, but we know that there are patients coming to the ER that can't get in because our beds are full," he continued. "And some of the physicians are telling us the same thing about not being able to get their private patients in."

Together we decided on a plan of action. By 9:00 a.m., we had gathered the VP for nursing and the director of facilities. We went to the top floor with the intent of working our way down. Within a few minutes on the 13th floor we had found five rooms being used by various staff that could be easily converted back to patient rooms and one that needed some minor renovations before being put back into service. We had to find a place for the staff and for the family medicine residents we were about to displace, but within an hour that had been resolved. Before the morning was over we had identified rooms for 24 beds and had decided to do a quick face lift of a 20 bed wing that was in dormancy awaiting a major renovation scheduled for a year or so away. The results were impressive. As soon as a room was ready, there was a patient for the bed. The financial picture turned around just as quickly. The lesson—always listen when the CFO says, "we need to talk."

-Stephen C. Schimpff, MD

The emergency room in many ways was the "front door" to the hospital. Not only did many emergency room patients end up being admitted to the hospital, but many faculty physicians would send their patients directly from their office to the emergency room to be further evaluated before admission. In general, everyone recognized that this was a more efficient method of getting needed laboratory tests and imaging done. As an addition to this "front door," Barish suggested the creation of a program to be known as Express Care. The basic concept was that the hospital would contract to have an ambulance positioned by the emergency department with a driver and a paramedic on duty. A call center was developed and was available around the clock, seven days a week. A referring physician could call this number from anywhere in the state or region, indicating that he or she had a patient to refer to UMMS, and the Express Care ambulance would be dispatched immediately to pick up the patient and bring him or her back to the hospital. This led to a major enhancement in admissions. The concept was that Express Care would contact a faculty attending (on call by beeper 24/7) to respond immediately to Express Care and talk with the referring physician about the transfer. This was critical because until that time referring physicians needed to make upwards of seven calls to arrange a transfer, generally having to negotiate with a resident (whose last desire was to accept more work for himself or for his colleagues!). Community physicians did not want to haggle with residents; either the process was prompt or they would call another tertiary hospital. The result was that the Express Care call center would contact the appropriate attending physician, get that individual connected with the referring physician, stay on the line to get agreement and then dispatch the ambulance. It took a long time for the medical school faculty to recognize the importance of being available and responsive, but in time Express Care became one of the most effective mechanisms for enhancing hospital admissions and for pleasing referring physicians.

After a few years a special addition was made for children, and then an Express Care team was stationed on the eastern shore of Maryland for faster service in that region. More recently, helicopter transport was added through a contractual relationship with a private carrier. Overall, Express Care proved to be a valuable service for the community physicians and for the medical center with more than 8,000 patient transports per year. These proved to be high-intensity, complex-tertiary and quaternary-care patients, helping to significantly increase the hospital's case mix index and drive up operating revenues.

Meanwhile, there was only so much money to invest in renovation of facilities. Prioritization was necessary and essential; but what was to be the highest priority? The decision was made by Rapoport and Schimpff to place the vast majority of the available money from First Chicago into renovations of inpatient clinical services, such as medicine, surgery, pediatrics and so forth. This meant that major support to services like radiology and the clinical laboratories and the outpatient clinics would have to wait. In short, the concept was that the clinical services were key to improving the number of admissions, which in turn were key to improving net income, which in turn would improve the ability to borrow funds for further renovations. For the same reasons, the decision was made to delay improvements to the cafeteria and kitchen and to the elevators, despite the faculty and staff frustrations noted previously. But food services clearly needed an upgrade and eventually an off balance-sheet approach was found by outsourcing that service to a private vendor who then re-capitalized the terribly outmoded kitchen along with a total renovation of the dining area for the cafeteria. This project was thus completed at least five to seven years sooner than it would have been otherwise had it been necessary to wait for its place in the capital queue.

LESSONS LEARNED:

Having a board of directors that was experienced, focused and committed was of exceptional value, especially in the early days after the governance change. But the legislation that created the medical system had left it with some nagging issues including the pension gap, the dual personnel system, the lack of vote for the university members of the board and the complicated and vague relationship of Shock Trauma relative to the overall System. These three issues, each a result of the legislation process, began to extract substantial time and energy from the leadership of the medical system and, quite frankly, led to tensions, controversy and difficulties in management. In retrospect these might have been predicted and prevented, but hindsight is not reality; reality would need to be addressed, and soon.

CHAPTER SIX

Major Tensions Erupt—
The School-Yard Bullies

A decade without campus leadership followed Farmer's death in 1984 on the day the legislation was passed creating the medical system. Eight presidents or acting presidents[4] served over a 10-year span; one was even appointed but left on his very first day of work. This lack of a consistent leader for UMAB hampered the development of partnerships with both the school of medicine and the university as a whole. It was difficult to solve problems, and it was difficult to determine who was in charge.

The medical school leadership had objected from the beginning to the fact that the dean was on the board of directors of the medical system but without vote. The dean (Dennis) described it in a published article as similar to "howling in the wind," where no one was listening, nor could anyone hear.

Concurrently the clinical chiefs wanted a greater role in directing the management decisions for their hospital. The chairs/chiefs were accustomed to a large degree of autonomy and authority. Indeed, the chairs in the medical school held substantial power as they and their faculty brought in most of the school's funding in the form of research

---

NOTES:

4. Until 1984 the senior leadership position of the University of Maryland at Baltimore (UMAB) was entitled *chancellor*. With a reorganization of the entire University System of Maryland and its 13 campuses across the state, the system leadership position was changed to *chancellor* and the individual campus leadership positions were given the title *president*. Hence, Farmer was the *chancellor*, but his successors carried the title *president*. And, in the late 1990s, the Baltimore campus changed its name to University of Maryland Baltimore (UMB).

grants and clinical income. This might be termed an "inverted power structure." In short, the dean and the chiefs did not like the fact that the board of directors was the final authority to choose the chief executive officer, to approve the budget and to approve clinical program development decisions. Frankly, they wanted a return to pre-governance times when, through the dean, they could exert substantial direct control over the management of University Hospital.

In 1987, two of the chiefs, acting on behalf of a larger number, met one evening with Rapoport and indicated that the chiefs had lost confidence in his leadership and encouraged him to resign. Rapoport met with the board chairman immediately and asked that the board make a decision as to his employment. The board took the charges seriously and set up a meeting with all of the clinical leadership and the board chair, with Rapoport and Schimpff in attendance. The chiefs filed into the board room, each in a freshly washed and pressed white coat, and took their seats. Kastor, the chairman of medicine, took the lead to outline the reasons for their dissatisfaction and then each clinical chief read a short prepared statement on one issue or another that was of concern to them. The board, at the urging of the president, Edward N. Brandt, MD, then decided to engage three outside academic medical leaders to do an evaluation. This took some months to arrange and conduct, with tensions high in the interim. The consultants did not recommend Rapoport's dismissal, but did have some specific suggestions as to changes in his management style and in how the board could maintain an ongoing dialogue with the clinicians. In effect, they urged better alignment with the school and the clinical faculty. The ultimate resolution was multifaceted. Since Schimpff had a generally good rapport with the chiefs, he was to spend increased time with them. The board would engage the clinical leadership through membership on various committees including strategic planning, technology and capital planning. The board also understood from the beginning that this was not just an issue of whether a particular individual should or should not be dismissed. Rather it was an issue of who had the ultimate authority to make decisions within this new medical system—the chiefs/dean or the board of directors. It was a fundamental governance question and the board recognized its responsibility to be in charge while at the same time giving legitimate opportunities to the chiefs to make their case.

Keep Your Antenna Up

I was in Connecticut with our daughter who was looking at various colleges. She stayed overnight in a dormitory, and I was in a motel. At 7:00 a.m., the phone rang; it was Mort. He told me of the two chiefs stopping at his office the prior evening and recommending that he resign. They had indicated that this was the view of many of the chiefs and implied that it was nearly universal. I was first distraught for Mort. He had worked exceptionally hard under the most difficult of conditions to bring about the needed changes and allow the medical system to thrive. But as I began to reflect, I also became concerned that I had not detected any "rumblings" and should have if I was doing my job well. I had good rapport with most of the chairs, was invited to many of their parties and thought I understood their needs—even if all could not be granted given the level of financial wherewithal the system had at that time. How could it be that I had missed this level of dissatisfaction? The message was clear: spend more time with individual chairs and with the group, listen to them and understand their needs and aspirations. Help them where possible and show them how to help themselves by creating more value within the system. Keep your antenna up all the time. And spend more time with the dean and his staff to understand what their thoughts were on all the important issues confronting the two institutions.

-Stephen C. Schimpff, MD

Bray, a member of the national advisory committee, commented "everyone has a boss somewhere," and that the chiefs would have to recognize that the board, not them, would have the ultimate decision-making authority for the medical system. Challoner, another member of the board, upon reading the report of the chiefs labeled it "puerile." But the chiefs did not see it that way. They had goals that were essentially identical to those of Rapoport, but Kastor saw a different means to achieve the ends, and he wanted to achieve them now. He wanted to take charge and believed that the chair of medicine should be the power broker in an academic medical center. This was in contrast to Rapoport, who recognized that progress would be inherently slower than desired but that patience was critical—essential to success. UMMS was still developing credibility with various constituencies, such as the business community, the legislative community and the executive branch of state government. The board felt Kastor's approach was essentially a "scorched earth" approach that would tear down everything in an attempt to create renewal. The board believed that if the medical system was "torn down" no one would step up to rebuild it; it would just stay torn down for some time.

This was an organizational dilemma. Many thought it was just an interpersonal struggle, but others like Gunther and Butta saw it as an organizational struggle. They recognized that it needed resolution in order to create an orderly system. So in the end the advice of the outside advisory group—that Rapoport should remain in place but needed to make changes in how he managed and work harder to seek consensus—was the course of the day. Schimpff's role became the "binder" between management and the physicians. He became a stabilizing factor, given that Rapoport's supporters were at best a quiet minority at that time. So Schimpff was charged to make relationships work with the physicians while Rapoport concentrated on building the credibility issues with various outside constituencies. Rapoport appreciated that his manner was sometimes confrontational, but as he assessed the situation he came to strongly believe that alignment—partnership and collaboration—was critical for success. It had already begun to work with the state government, and it could or at least should work with the faculty physicians. This approach was more natural for Schimpff, Chrencik and Ashworth, but Rapoport's message to his management team was that it would become the institutional leadership culture henceforth.

Alignment meant understanding the other party's agenda, mission, and vision. It did not mean that every request would be granted; indeed it could not be given the resource limitations. But it did mean developing partnerships and collaborating wherever possible. Members of the leadership team also worked on developing personal relationships. These were valuable and important but alignment trumped relationships in that relationships were not sufficient to advance the strategies and agenda if there was not alignment first.

R Adams Cowley, My Friend

No book about the University of Maryland Hospital is complete without recalling some of the many, many personal experiences and stories that involve Cowley. Our relationship began when I was a medical student

R Adams Cowley, MD

and served an elective when Cowley was preparing to open a two-bed clinical shock and trauma unit in the department of surgery. At the time Cowley was head of cardio-thoracic surgery, but his focus and passion was on the study of shock-related injury. I would renew my relationship with Cowley six years later when I returned to the University of Maryland in 1967 after six years in the U.S. Army Medical Corps. I returned as an assistant professor of medicine in the division of infectious diseases. Since Theodore E. Woodward, MD, then chairman of medicine, needed additional salary support to recruit me he asked Cowley to pay one half of my salary; in return I served half time in the developing Shock Trauma. By now the unit was a 16-bed acute care unit located on the fourth floor of the hospital. My research interests at that time were the study of metabolic changes in infection and that interested Cowley, but he also wanted clinical support in his unit beyond the traditional general surgeons, anesthesiologists, neurosurgeons and orthopedic surgeons that he had recruited. I became the first internist to work in Shock Trauma. My exposure to Cowley and his colleagues was among the most exciting and rewarding periods in my professional life. For almost three years I found myself working with an "out of the box" leader who loved to challenge traditional approaches and strategies. He inevitably found himself in conflict with his peers who did not share his vision for the multi-specialty or multi-disciplinary care for trauma-related illnesses. But he stimulated his faculty and his team, and as a result the faculty was both loyal and dedicated to a fault. As a result of my experience with Cowley, I became his advocate and devotee, and my devotion continues even to today. During my years as associate dean of the medical school and then as CEO of the medical system, I looked to Cowley for counsel and sage advice. One of my greatest disappointments in life was his alignment with the clinical chairmen and the dean when they requested my resignation in 1987.

What was absolutely astounding was his conversation with me when I asked him how he could align against me with people he disliked and for whom he had no respect? His response was one for the books. In fact, it was ironic.

He said, "You are my friend; you don't want to work with these idiots. They don't appreciate what you've done, and besides you can resign and come work for me. I'll make you my number two, and you will succeed me when I retire."

I smiled and thanked him for his confidence. He was always "out of the box," and his thinking and behavior was beyond my capacity to comprehend. I often wonder whether he was serious and what might have happened had I done what he suggested.

-Morton I. Rapoport, MD

Another key issue during those early years after the creation of the medical system, was the perceived needs and aspirations of African-American members of the board of directors. In 1985, Eli Saunders, MD, an early African American graduate of the University of Maryland School of Medicine and a highly respected cardiologist in the community, became vice president for graduate medical education and concurrently the head of the division of hypertension in the department of medicine. In about 1987, Saunders told Schimpff that he observed overt racism among some medical residents and some attending physicians. It was subtle stuff, such as an attending calling only upon the white residents or the white students on morning rounds. Although the patient population consisted of a large proportion of African Americans, relatively few African Americans were among the resident staff. Russell, an African-American board member who was a senior lawyer at a major law firm and former Baltimore City solicitor, took it upon himself to meet one by one with each clinical chief over breakfast to discuss the issue of recruiting African Americans into the residency programs. In general he got a good response, and many of the chiefs appreciated his insights. The result was that over the next few years African-American staff steadily increased.

But not all understood the issue at hand; the head of a surgical subspecialty division responded by saying, "Our specialty is very competitive; we only take the very best."

Muldrow, another African-American board member and CEO of the Development Credit Fund—an organization supported by the banking community to make affordable loans to small businesses owned by minority citizens—became chair of the facilities committee of the board. The Shock Trauma building had been recently finished, the loans from First Chicago were being used to do renovations in the south hospital building and the master facility plan was underway. Schimpff introduced Muldrow to the vice president for facilities, Dennis Schrader, who then worked with Muldrow to make the contracting opportunities more open to minority businesses. Schrader took an aggressive step and hired an African-American woman to run the major construction projects in 1990. She established a relationship with a major national contractor who had developed a "contractor's college." The medical system adopted the program which met weekly in the evening and reviewed with the potential contractors how the medical system did business, what projects were upcoming and how an individual contractor could enter a proposal or bid. Since some small contractors were relatively unknown, and the state of their workmanship was likewise unknown, Schrader would offer small projects with the dual purpose of introducing the contractor to the medical system and concurrently having the opportunity to observe the quality of workmanship, commitment to schedule and other important factors. This gave the contractor and the medical system greater future opportunities. Later, when the Gudelsky Building was built, the medical system required that each aspirant to be the general contractor consist of a major well-known contractor teamed with a first-class minority contractor. Ultimately the Gudelsky Building was completed with 30 percent of the funding going to minority subcontractors. Schrader also joined the council for economic and business development, a city focused, but statewide group created to assist minority businesses in the Baltimore area. Schrader eventually became chair of the group and this helped to steer quality minority-owned businesses to the medical system.

Meanwhile a concerted effort sought to improve the amount of purchasing done through minority vendors. To some degree this was difficult because most purchases were made through large national vendors, such as Baxter or Johnson & Johnson for medical supplies, the Red Cross for blood products and a few major wholesalers for drugs. But Dennis Grote, director of operations, put extensive effort into finding ways to increase the medical system's purchases through minority vendors. These included partnering with minority distributors with major suppliers and literally assisting in the creation of new minority owned firms capable of effectively responding to the competitive marketplace. The result was a marked increase in purchasing dollars spent with minority-owned firms.[5]

A simmering issue with the school was the long held organizational arrangement of departments based upon faculty training disciplines (e.g., medicine, surgery) contrasted to the developing need to care for patients with complex, chronic illnesses in a disease or multidisciplinary manner (as exemplified by Shock Trauma and the cancer center). This was in the late 1980s when Shock Trauma was growing rapidly and earned an imposing statewide reputation for having a truly remarkable 97% survival rate for all patients brought to it. This was particularly impressive given that only the four to five percent of all trauma patients who had the

NOTES:

5. Schimpff SC, Rapoport MI, O'Keefe SL, Grote DA, Snow LK, "The University of Maryland Medical System Invests in its Community's Minorities," *Academic Medicine* 1996, 71: 604-612.

Shock Trauma, 1989

most severe injuries were brought to Shock Trauma. But as noted earlier, the tradition in the school of medicine was a discipline orientation around departments of medicine, surgery and anesthesia. This was the way students and residents were educated and trained, and it was the way the faculty was organized. But in Shock Trauma's tradition, general surgeons, orthopedic surgeons, neurosurgeons, infectious disease internists and critical care internists along with anesthesiologists all worked together to care for the patient. Shock Trauma had its own practice plan, which included all of the involved specialists; this was anathema to the department chairs. Particularly, there was a standoff between the departments of surgery where Shock Trauma had originated and where Cowley had been a noted cardiothoracic surgeon. Joseph McLaughlin, MD, himself a cardiothoracic surgeon and longtime colleague of Cowley, became head of thoracic surgery after Cowley focused fully on MIEMSS and then McLaughlin became chair of surgery in 1982. Despite his long association with Cowley, the two could not overcome the long-standing tensions, although they, along with the dean (Dennis), found ways to co-exist without major turmoil. In effect, Cowley and McLaughlin had a good personal relationship, but their approach to organizational structure was not in alignment.

Shock Trauma took responsibility for the salaries of its staff, but each physician required a faculty appointment in a school department. Not being "regular" members of the department, however, meant that surgeons in the trauma center were often not promoted as would be the case otherwise. An example was Anthony Burgess, MD, head of trauma orthopedics. He held the faculty title of instructor (the lowest possible rank) at the school of medicine but was granted an associate professor-level appointment at Johns Hopkins for his volunteer work there. He liked to note to others that he was considered of higher stature at Hopkins, one of the best-ranked schools in the country, whereas he was given short shrift at his own institution simply because he worked within Shock Trauma.

Orthopedics became essentially two divisions, one in Shock Trauma and one in surgery, with separate practice plans although all were ostensibly faculty in a single division. Residents rotated through the two programs as though they were one, and in fact the program in Shock Trauma was highly regarded by resident applicants. Anesthesiology was equally troubled with a staff in Shock Trauma that had faculty appointments in the department of anesthesiology but little else to bind them together. Shock Trauma used nurse anesthetists routinely, but the department would not tolerate them in the "hospital" ORs. Trauma had a group of critical care physicians who were internists but had essentially no affiliation with the department of medicine—unlike the infectious disease group that maintained a close relationship with the other members of the department of medicine's ID division. Such was the state of affairs for many years—one that we have termed the *Twenty-Year War*.

Meanwhile a similar disease versus discipline issue plagued the cancer center. In 1974, the NCI moved its BCRC from the Public Health Service Hospital, which was being closed by presidential order, into University Hospital and the adjacent new medical school research tower named the Bressler Research Building. Both buildings had vacant floors. The NCI rented the ninth floor of both buildings and eventually built a bridge connecting the basic science laboratories with the clinical floor. The staff consisted of physicians and scientists who were federal employees of the NCI along with support staff of nurses, social workers and others who were employees of the university. In 1981 the NCI decided to terminate the BCRC, and the university decided to use the opportunity to establish a university-based cancer center. Schimpff, a 13-year employee of the NCI, was asked to direct the new University of Maryland Cancer Center. Initially, the school of medicine dean, university chancellor and the CEO of the newly created and still University-based UMMS agreed that it would function as a center with a disease orientation. Physicians would have faculty appointments in the appropriate campus school or departments, many in the department of medicine but also in pharmacology, biochemistry, pathology, microbiology, and psychiatry along with the schools of dentistry and pharmacy. But if the Shock Trauma story was essentially a *Twenty-Year War* the cancer center now soon entered a *Ten-Year War*. Kastor, the newly-arrived chairman of the department of medicine, saw the cancer center as essentially a division of oncology within the department of medicine. Upon accepting his position, he was promised by the dean (Dennis) that, among other things, the center's practice plan would be disbanded, and the internists would work through a newly revitalized department of medicine practice plan. The struggle slowed down program development, prevented applying for a core grant and led to rapid turnover of directors (three in seven years) and the inability to recruit a strong outside director. The issue was eventually resolved after a new dean, Donald E. Wilson, MD, MACP, arrived. Meetings with Moxley, a former dean and now national search firm consultant, and external advisors emphasized that the cancer center needed autonomy, a separate practice plan, authority over space, recruitments and hiring. Wilson accepted these recommendations, and the changes were made, making it possible to recruit a director. These were necessary but not totally sufficient arrangements to ensure success of the cancer center.

LESSONS LEARNED:

Alignment is critical in an academic medical center. In retrospect it became evident that, in the face of what seemed like overwhelming obstacles to assure a functioning enterprise and all that this entailed, alignment with the faculty physicians had been placed on the "back burner." This, coupled with the antipathy of the dean to the structural change that had occurred with the governance change, led to an unfortunate standoff. The board showed its mettle by first listening carefully to the faculty physicians and understanding their concerns and frustrations but then insisting that it and it alone was the ultimate decision maker. The key lesson was that alignment with the faculty physicians needed constant and intensive attention.

CHAPTER SEVEN

Strategic, Technology, Capital and Master Facility Planning— Toddlerhood to Adolescence

Roger Lipitz/Rosalie Rapoport "He has a Point"

Midway during Lipitz's tenure as board chairman, he had a conversation with me I will never forget.

Shortly after Wilson was named dean of the medical school and with a new president of the UMB campus expected to be named soon, Lipitz sat with me alone and said something like this: "Mort, you will have a new group of campus leaders to work with. It is not clear whether they will be easier or harder to collaborate with, but you have no choice. If you can't find a way to work with these new leaders, people, including your board members, will blame you. They will say 'no one can work with Mort.'"

Not surprisingly I was disappointed with the conversation. How could Roger say what he said? We had made great progress; I worked hard dealing effectively with a number of difficult and sometimes dysfunctional people; why was I now on trial? Why would I be held responsible if these new leaders failed to cooperate? That was basically the conversation I had with my wife, Rosalie. I repeated my conversation with Lipitz to her.

She listened patiently and then said, "You know, he has a point. You ought to give it some thought."

Naturally I was angry and felt she did not understand. We didn't talk for the next 24 to 48 hours. It was a tough weekend. But by Monday morning I called a meeting with Schimpff, Chrencik and Ashworth, my three top lead-

ers, and stated that for the next three years your entire incentive compensation will be based on our success and partnerships with campus leaders. We will partner with them whether they like it or not. In fact we made campus collaboration a key factor in incentive compensation for the next 10 years. Indeed, this partnership strategy may have been the single most important success factor in creating alignment with the school of medicine.

-Morton I. Rapoport, MD

The medical system needed a clear vision, mission and strategic plan, one that all could embrace and work towards. Importantly, a plan embraced by the school and clinical faculty would benefit all parties. Also needed was resolution of the "disease versus discipline" dichotomy; one approach favored by the school and the other favored by the medical system.

The first few years of the medical system's existence were ones of survival, developing systems, recruiting and developing a leadership team throughout the organization, and investing the small amount of capital that came from the First Chicago line of credit. But by 1987 it was time to develop a comprehensive strategic plan—where was the medical system headed and how was it going to get there? The planning process unfolded with Lipitz agreeing to chair the strategic planning committee with Schimpff as the principal medical system leader. An outside consulting firm, APM, including one of its key partners, James Kagen, was chosen to assist with leadership. A large steering committee was created that included medical system board members, management members, the dean of the school of medicine, one of the other deans on campus, and six clinical chiefs plus a few additional faculty chosen because of their interest and influence. The steering committee met on a regular basis every few weeks, and the plan developed iteratively. A key decision by Schimpff was that the plan needed to be data-based, a transparent process among all members of the steering committee, with plenty of opportunity for debate and consideration. The consultants would put their data together for review by committee members in advance, present it at the meeting and then leave extensive time for debate.

The first steps developed a vision, a mission and a value statement for the medical system. The mission was straightforward and had three parts: patient care (tertiary care to the state and region and comprehensive care for the local community), education/training, and research – in that order. These are the same three elements as in the school of medicine's mission but with a distinctly different order. It was important to establish this first and get consensus and clarity among the clinical leadership, including the dean, because traditionally University Hospital had been perceived as existing principally as a site for the faculty to teach medical students and train residents. The discussion around mission also focused on how the medical system was or was not different from Johns Hopkins Hospital and how it differed from nearby community hospitals. The fact that more than 50% of the physicians practicing in Maryland were graduates of the medical school, the hospital residency programs or both whereas the corresponding number for Johns Hopkins was about 12% suggested a key difference. Hopkins students and residents came from across the country; most of those at university were from Maryland. Hopkins Hospital was active in recruiting patients from across the country and even internationally; Maryland was not. The medical system was thus a regional organization whereas Johns Hopkins saw itself as national in scope. The medical system with its university partnership was clearly a key state resource; it was the state's academic medical center.

The vision became clear: "In partnership with the University of Maryland School of Medicine, to be a standard-setting academic medical center, one that others would emulate."

The values statement was likewise straightforward, emphasizing those key qualities that the institution wanted to stand for: quality of care, excellence in service, respect for the individual, quality in education and research, and cost-effectiveness. The committee readily adopted the first four values, but the last one was a new concept. Many faculty members inherently believed that cost management was equivalent to quality reduction and were therefore hard to convince that being cost conscious need not equate with lesser quality of care. Ultimately, after much debate, that element of the value system was validated.

The next step was to prioritize the clinical programs for development. Clearly the medical system did not have sufficient funding to devote to each of the clinical programs. Program development demanded prioritization and an organized order. Working with Kagan, Schimpff decided that it would not be by department but rather by clinical program. So analyses were done for cardiac care, cancer care, mental health, neurocare, etc. for a total of 52 different clinical programs. (In effect this was disease-orientation rather than a discipline or departmental orientation.) Each was analyzed for what it would cost to bring it up to a reasonable level; how the program fit with the mission; what the local market size would be; whether there was room for a new competitor; what the return on investment would be and over what time frame; and, finally, whether the physicians would clearly support that program. This data-based analysis showed that the programs to focus on first were trauma, cancer, cardiac, neurocare, high-risk obstetrics and neonatology, orthopedics/rheumatology, and rehabilitation. However the tensions that existed between Shock Trauma and the department of surgery, each having a part of the orthopedics program, meant that investment in that program was impossible then. There was also concern that major investments in cancer should be delayed until the medical school accepted the multidisciplinary or disease-oriented rather than discipline-oriented strategy. Trauma care, neurocare, high-risk obstetrics and neonatology, and cardiac care ranked highest, and rehabilitation also ranked high because it was fed from and was a support to both trauma and neurocare. These concepts, with the accompanying data, were presented along with a commitment from the medical system leadership that as dollars were earned by the programs to be developed, those dollars would be invested into the next programs on the list. This gave everyone reason to believe that eventually their favorite program would be funded.

Development of some programs turned out to be highly expensive. The new trauma building was under construction and funded by the state; so development funds were not needed there. But the cardiac program required an additional cardiac operating room, a completely new cardiac surgical recovery room, a totally revamped cardiac catheterization laboratory, a new coronary care unit and a new progressive care unit along with recruitment of substantial numbers of faculty in surgery, medicine, radiology and elsewhere to round out a full program. Neuro-care needed a new ICU, a stepdown unit and substantial new equipment and instruments for the operating suite and an epilepsy unit along with added neurosurgeons and neurologists, especially in stroke and epilepsy care. It was clear that developing each of the selected programs would be expensive and could not be done all at once. Further, it was necessary that the medical system redouble its efforts to increase its net income and hence its cash flow and debt capacity.

Much of the strategic plan related to developing clinical programs resulting in increased revenues. But cost management was equally critical. Again with the assistance of APM, UMMS embarked on an "operations improvement" agenda. The basic idea was to break the institution into smaller and smaller parts for the purpose of analyzing opportunities for improving the way the hospital functioned with the expectation that improved quality would lead to reduced costs. But the cost implications needed to be definite and measurable. Managers at all levels were expected to participate and, working as teams, devise ways to overcome obstacles and barriers to success. They were expected to meet with the involved faculty chiefs and get their blessing before proceeding, or change the approach in a way that would obtain their endorsement. But the expectation of each manager was to find a defined level of cost savings while improving the hospital functions. The results were excellent in three ways. Costs were indeed substantially reduced. Operations were visibly improved. And by way of a bonus, it became clear which managers were up to the task of managing and which really had not made the conversion from the former "state mentality" to the new "enterprise management approach." As just one example, certain nurse directors found multiple ways to erect barriers to success and ultimately they left the organization. Conversely, McCullough, a particularly astute charge nurse, was able to find multiple ways to succeed with the operations improvement approach. She would some years later become the vice president for nursing and later still the senior vice president for patient care services and operations.

With Gunther not being reappointed to the board by Gov. Schaefer, Lipitz now took over as chair. Having been through the strategic planning process, he recognized the needs of the institution and that the facilities were clearly inadequate as was the technology base. His message to Rapoport emphasized that it was important to raise large sums of money for recapitalization of the medical system. His basic message was that major dollars would be needed and that Rapoport would be held accountable for the success of this endeavor. This would require not only going to the state for facility funding but also building a fundraising function as well. As a businessman with a good understanding of health care, he proved to be an excellent strategist for the medical system. To assist in strategizing for approaching the state for funding, Lipitz recommended that Richard "Rick" Berndt, Esq., managing partner of Gallagher, Evelius and Jones law firm, be engaged to help. Berndt had been close to Gov. Schaefer for many years, and his message was succinct—it was critical to get to everyone who might at some point be contacted by the governor and let them know about the need and the solution for the medical system's requirements. It was important to get their enthusiastic support or at least their tacit agreement that a request to the governor was reasonable. Then when the governor reached out to his colleagues, he would find only agreement. One at a time, about a dozen individuals were brought in to learn about the medical system, tour the current facilities and understand the strategic plan going forward. As it turned out, the governor did talk with just these individuals, and he received each one's individual support when asked.

The approach with Arthur Hilsenrad, head of the state capital planning office, was essentially the same. Invite him in, give him a tour, and help him understand the needs. In addition, treat him like a major donor. Having him understand the issues and commit to their resolution meant that he would also be supportive when approached by the governor.

Gov. Schaefer had been Baltimore's mayor, and he felt an affinity for the medical system and for the university overall. He saw that the two institutions mattered greatly to both the city and the entire state. He also felt that the west side of Baltimore could and should be revitalized, and that the two institutions were key to this revitalization. He was aware of the financial difficulties of the hospital over the years and was aware of the tension and conflict between the university leadership and Cowley, his friend at Shock Trauma. But, more importantly, he was a bricks and mortar person—he believed in reinvesting in the state with capital projects. All of this was to the medical system's advantage. Gov. Schaefer also knew Lipitz and had a good relationship with him. He knew many of the UMMS board members—particularly during his time as both city council president and then as mayor—and had implicit trust in their judgment. It was a time of good relationships. Gov. Schaefer was also committed to the concept of public/private partnerships; so this was consistent with his view as well.

The combination of a sound strategic plan, a master facilities plan, a capital plan, a supportive governor and legislature along with their desire for redevelopment of that area of Baltimore all worked together to launch the second phase of capital development of the medical system.

It is worth noting that state government officials and university officials over the years were frequently at odds with each other. Of necessity, the university was always looking for more money, and the state, of necessity, was always looking for ways to regulate the process. In the years immediately preceding formation of UMMS, the then-director of the hospital and the hospital's external legal counsel took a generally adversarial approach with the state officials, the HSCRC and others. The approach changed dramatically under the new medical system leadership. State officials needed to be considered colleagues and treated as such. In the end, UMMS leadership used this approach in all relationships. Partnership (alignment) was the basic theme.

Recall that phase I had been a combination of Shock Trauma, funded largely by the state, along with the renovations to the south hospital and to a lesser degree the north hospital, funded by the First Chicago line of credit along with the retained earnings from operations. Rapoport named this "phase I of the public/private partnership," in which the state had contributed about one-third of the dollars and the medical system about two-thirds. It was now time to address phase II. A master facilities plan in 1988 laid out with the assistance of RTKL Architects demonstrated exactly what was needed. There were two approaches. One suggested extensive renovations in the current complex of buildings making up the medical system, and the second advocated construction of a new building along with renovations. Some argued that it was possible to fit all of the needs into the older buildings, but Rapoport was adamant that it was critical to proceed with an added new building and that to not do so "would consign the medical system to mediocrity for at least the next 10 to 20 years." The new building would have at least four purposes. The first was to create added clinical space for needed services, built for current and future technologies. The second was to change the image of the medical system and make a clear statement to the community that **it** had come of age and was a force to be reckoned with in Baltimore and in the region. The third was to break the image, albeit an incorrect image, of the medical system as essentially an indigent care hospital. Finally, the building needed to be designed in such a way that it created a truly caring and uplifting environment.

Homer Gudelsky had been a patient in the cancer center, and he and his wife, Martha, were very impressed with the care that he received. Gudelsky had been referred to UMMS at the urging of his friend Leonard Berger, MD, a good friend and classmate in medical school of Rapoport. A few years later the Gudelskys donated $1 million to the medical system toward the purchase of an MRI and the necessary renovations to house it. Now with the master facility plan complete, Rapoport took Schimpff with him to propose that the Gudelsky family participate as the lead gift toward the ambitious capital program of the medical system. The phase II capital plan called for $125 million. The Gudelskys donated $5 million, the state ultimately gave $65 million and other gifts amounted to an additional $22 million with the remainder coming from a bond issuance and retained net income.

The Gudelsky Building opened to critical acclaim in 1994. It clearly met the needs of added space for needed services consistent with new technology requirements; it definitively changed the image of UMMS within the community; it now became clear that it was not an indigent

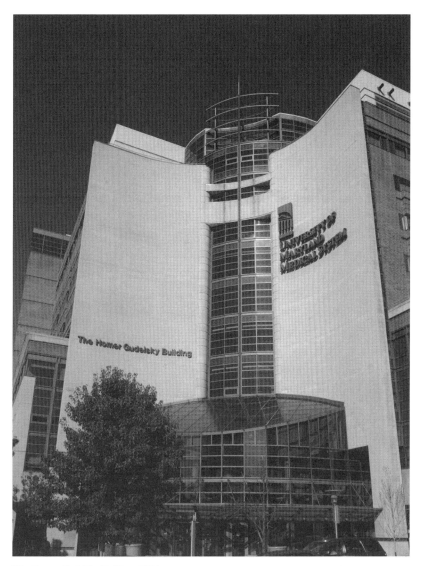

The Homer Gudelsky Building, 1994

care hospital; and everyone agreed that the new building designed by Zeidler and Associates with its soaring nine-story internal atrium created 'a particularly caring and uplifting environment. A good example of the latter was the decision for placement of radiation oncology. Traditionally, radiation oncology is in the basement because of the need for shielding the electron beam units. So radiation oncology was below ground, but the waiting room was built just below the front door such that people sitting in the waiting room looked up to an entry atrium that rose for three floors with a glass walkway that carried visitors from the front door across and into the lobby with its atrium. Patients waited in an open, airy and sunny location where they could watch activity both inside the building and outside on the sidewalks and street. This added a sense of hope and comfort for the patients. Indeed the completion of the building and all that it included led to a change of internal culture, one where everyone who worked in the hospital believed that "this was a really good place." It also helped faculty and staff to understand that UMMS did not need to be in the shadow of Hopkins as many believed. The mission and vision were different; the institution was successful and confident; and it had garnered public support in the form of fund-raised dollars, access to the bond markets and state collaborations.

Sen. Kelly would later tell his former legislative colleagues, "You got a terrific deal here. By your privatizing the hospital, it has found a way to put up more than two-thirds of the cost of its recapitalization whereas the state only had to put up less than one-third. If we had not privatized it when we did 10 years ago in 1984, the state would have eventually had to pay for the whole thing—or it would never have been done!"

It was important for the medical system to also understand that the medical school was actively working on its research building space needs. It had consistently demonstrated that when the school obtained more space it was able to recruit outstanding faculty to expand the research base for the School. So whenever the medical system presented its plans to legislators or others it always included in its renderings the school's planned health science facility. And in return, the school included the Gudelsky Building in its plans for the new research building.

At about this time, Stewart Greenebaum replaced Lipitz as board chair. He likewise appreciated the need to align with the school of medicine leadership. Indeed, he looked to develop his own personal relationship with Wilson, recently-appointed dean. He agreed with Rapoport's view that the medical system was now clearly on its way toward success and that long-lasting success depended on an alignment with the school. Greenebaum was also an expansionist. As a first step he pushed for an offsite ambulatory care center similar to a Johns Hopkins building to the north of Baltimore known as "Greenspring Station." He learned from the ongoing strategic planning activities that this was an important approach to the future of referrals to the hospital and the physicians' practice. The concept was simple—patients would come downtown for major needs, such as open-heart surgery, kidney transplantation or complex cancer care, but they would not come downtown for more routine specialty care. If the medical system and the faculty wanted to assure those types of referrals and also to provide specialty care to those living outside the city, then it was necessary to go to them rather than to expect patients to come to the physicians. Appreciating this concept, he donated (as part of a larger gift to be described elsewhere) 17 acres directly off of Interstate 97, about two-thirds of the way from Baltimore to Annapolis. The site, in an area known as Shipley's Choice, was an ideal location, and shortly a building was constructed.

Concurrently, an approach was made to the Anne Arundel Health System to partner at Shipley's Choice. The idea contemplated was that the medical system and the medical school would place specialists and sub-specialists there, but that local physicians could rent space for primary and secondary care. Eventually the medical system ambulatory building rented about three-quarters of its space to community physicians and about one-quarter to faculty physicians.

Dinner with the Maulls

On frequent occasions my wife, Rosalie, and I had dinner with new recruits and their wives. On more than one occasion I would invite Rosalie to join with me and a prospective chairman or academic leader we were recruiting. I found her observations and her comments frequently helpful as we tried to determine the fit between the needs of our organization and that of the prospect. I occasionally regretted not having involved Rosalie earlier in the process. Our first dinner together with the Maulls was one

*of those occasions. Kimball Maull, MD, had been recruited to Maryland
to head MIEMSS. He was a well-known trauma surgeon from the University of Tennessee who enjoyed a reputation as a strong, no-nonsense
leader. He came with a reputation for having been involved in academic
conflict and controversy in several institutions. Indeed, many of those who
interviewed him and examined his credentials believed he had great similar-
ity to the late Cowley, the man he would succeed. Rosalie and I had dinner
with Kimball and his wife several weeks after we had come to terms with
him and his new position as head of MIEMSS and Shock Trauma. The
dinner seemed pleasant enough—good food, good conversation and lasting
almost three hours.*

*On the way home Rosalie said, "Tell me again, what is Dr. Maull's
role going to be?"*

*I said he was our new R A. Cowley. Rosalie had met Cowley on
several occasions and found him to be a very charming man; that was not
an opinion that I shared, but I could understand her observations. Many
women found Cowley charming.*

Again I asked, "What do you think?"

*She said, "Well I have three simple observations. First, the Maulls are
a very attractive couple, second he is no R A. Cowley and third he talked
about himself almost continuously for two hours."*

*We both agreed that he seemed anxious to impress us with his leader-
ship skills. Rosalie concluded her comments about the dinner by telling me,
"Good luck."*

*Less than two years later Maull resigned his position after endless lead-
ership conflicts at all levels and antagonizing virtually all of Shock Trauma
and MIEMSS stakeholders.*

-Morton I. Rapoport, MD

Donald E. Wilson, MD, MACP, was appointed the new dean in 1991.
David Ramsey, DM, DPhil, was appointed president of the university
three years later. Both remained in their positions for well over a decade,
and thus it became possible to begin working on alignment. One of the
first big issues to be solved was the relationship of Shock Trauma to the
school of medicine. A standoff continued between the department of

surgery, in particular, and Shock Trauma. Cowley had been the vision-ary for Shock Trauma, and Ashworth, his right-hand operating officer, had been the architect in not only putting together the center itself but the statewide system of transportation and communication along with developing the political clout of MIEMSS. From 1989 on, Ashworth had become a senior vice president at the medical system, reporting to Schimpff, in charge of the master facility plan, the strategic plan, the building program and business development.

After Cowley retired, a lot of controversy and tension within Shock Trauma itself and within MIEMSS surfaced; a healer was needed. James P.G. "Seamus" Flynn, MD, was asked to take the helm on an interim basis. Flynn had been medical director and then CEO of Montebello Rehabilitation Hospital and had worked closely with Cowley and the trauma physicians. Flynn spent two years trying to stabilize the center, but many within were not prepared to become partners in a new ap-proach. But it must be emphasized that many in the school of medicine were even less willing to find a way for Shock Trauma to be an integral part of the whole. Eventually, a national search led to the recruitment and appointment of Maull as the director of MIEMSS and of Shock Trauma. But a variety of events led to his resignation within two years. Controversy reigned over his style and decisions on how to manage both the EMS system and the trauma center. With Maull's resignation, Ash-worth became director of Shock Trauma, an appointment that required the governor's blessing. He had immediate credibility with the governor and key legislators including Sen. Kelly, and he was well known by the trauma clinicians. Soon after Maull's departure, the legislature decided to split the trauma system into two parts. One element would be Shock Trauma which would be part of the medical system. The other element, MIEMSS—with its transportation and communication functions—would be organized as a state agency outside the university although it would have its offices on the university campus. This proved to be a good arrangement for the medical system as it meant Shock Trauma now had an arms-length relationship with MIEMSS and therefore received patients on a merit or protocol basis. This eliminated the concern of the level II trauma centers around the state that Shock Trauma was receiving more than its appropriate share of patients.

In 1997, Thomas Scalea, MD, was recruited from New York City to be clinical director of Shock Trauma. A few months later Bruce Jarrell, MD, was recruited from Arizona to be chairman of the department of surgery. Within weeks of Jarrell's arrival he and Scalea met to discuss how to end the longstanding tensions. Jarrell proposed to Scalea that Burgess, Shock Trauma's chief of orthopedics, become the head of a combined orthopedics unit. This would end the long festering issue of "two" divisions of orthopedics within the same institution. Jarrell also proposed to the dean that orthopedics become a department outside of surgery. The medical system agreed to add extra funding to facilitate the conversion. As a further concession, Jarrell offered Scalea the option of Shock Trauma surgeons taking emergency general surgery call; so that they could have surgical experiences other than just trauma surgery. The agreement was that the trauma surgeons would keep whatever earnings were generated, and UMMS agreed to add additional financial support. It was not all "peaches and cream," however, as Jarrell decided to keep the accounts receivable from orthopedics; this left trauma with a sizable deficit which the medical center was then asked to support, and it strained the relationship between Jarrell and Scalea for some time. But overall, a new dawn was emerging in regard to the trauma *Twenty-Year War*.

It is important to note that Maryland is the only state in the United States that has an EMS agency that is separate within the state government. Others are buried in various parts of state government, usually the health department, and cannot act as effectively as the current EMS system in Maryland. It began, as noted earlier, within the health department, but by 1978 new legislation established the new agency, called MIEMSS, within the university with Cowley directing both the statewide EMS system and Shock Trauma. Its placement within the university was in part because the university personnel system was less burdensome than the state personnel system—it was actually more flexible given that it was still part of the state system. Further, Neil Solomon, MD, secretary of health and mental hygiene at the time, was not a strong supporter of trauma from Cowley's perspective, and so Cowley was happy to move.

When the new Shock Trauma building was under consideration, the certificate of need anticipated about 3,500 admissions per year. The building opened in 1988, and within a decade it was admitting about 7,500 patients. The length of stay (LOS) had been reduced substantially, thereby opening beds for more patients to be admitted. Initially the LOS came down because of changes in medical care and procedures. For example, new technology in orthopedics allowed for much-reduced LOS for patients with severe bone injuries, representing about 60% of all trauma patients. Diagnostic technologies also allowed for shorter stays. But when LOS leveled out, patients in the state still needed to be admitted to the center. Since no more beds were available, the only way to create space for them was to further reduce LOS. In about 2001, Scalea instituted a program of early morning rounds—not the usual teaching or care rounds but rounds specifically focused on how to do whatever was needed to get a patient ready for discharge. He might, for example, ask those on rounds with him what a patient needed done.

The answer might be: "A CT scan."

Scalea would then respond: "Fine, but who is responsible for seeing the CT scan is done—this morning?"

Getting no response, he would deputize someone to take that responsibility and then hold them accountable tomorrow morning. Within one month he had reduced LOS by more than 10%, opening beds and allowing more patients to be admitted. And, of course, it was a quality enhancement step for the patients since they got out of the hospital sooner, not being held back because one test or another had not been completed. The only downside, from the medical center perspective, was that the HSCRC rate system paid a higher rate for trauma patients and reduced LOS meant a reduced charge for those patients. But better patient care trumped money, and the decision was not to back up. This was much better for the patients and meant more patients could be admitted. It was a "win-win" for care if not for the hospital's coffers.

Another issue was that of surgical critical care. Again both the department of surgery and Shock Trauma overlapped in that both wanted to train surgeons in the area of critical care. Furthermore, it was an issue for the department of anesthesiology because critical care was one of its key training programs, and it overlapped with both its own department and that of Shock Trauma. But one other underlying issue emerged as well. Scalea wanted to encourage the referral of critical care patients other than trauma. For example, he and his colleagues were building a practice around a serious disease called necrotizing fasciitis—basically a rapidly progressive infection usually caused by a streptococcus that advanced through tissues and caused their destruction. The creator of the Muppets, Jim Henson, had recently died from this disease. To some, this meant that Shock Trauma was taking advantage of its special relationship with the EMS community to attract even more patients away from other hospitals. To Scalea it was simply his desire to care for the very ill no matter what the origin or their illness.

As to the training issue, 12 critical care fellowship slots existed between surgery and Shock Trauma. These needed a leader to drive the program. Scalea and Jarrell recruited Stephen Johnson, MD, from Tucson (from where Jarrell had been recruited) to lead the program with his primary appointment in surgery but his principal work site to be Shock Trauma. His job was to pull all of the critical care programs together into a whole for the benefit of all and to assure that the training was first class. One of the key attributes for patient care under the new arrangement was that a physician was always available for those patients in need even when their primary surgeon was in the OR working on a new case.

It is important to realize that trauma is a business line with limited competition for the medical system. If it's serious trauma, it's brought to Shock Trauma. Only those with severe burns go to Hopkins Bayview Burn Center and children with severe trauma go to Johns Hopkins Hospital. Shock Trauma has a special rate structure with the HSCRC. The center is highly recognized across the state by the media and by legislators. The legislature has traditionally had a champion in Sen. Kelly, and after "Dutch" Ruppersberger (once a patient of Shock Trauma) became a congressman, Shock Trauma has had support there as well. In essence, the State of Maryland has determined that it has an obligation to assist with trauma, especially trauma that occurs on its roadways. It has funded Shock Trauma; the transportation system including the purchase, maintenance and staffing by state troopers of 12 helicopters at eight sites around the state; and has funded the communication system, all of which make up MIEMSS.

Cancer, unlike trauma, definitely does not have limited competition; it requires a strong program to compete for referrals from the state and region. But strong programs need financial support, and the cancer center was chronically underfunded. Rapoport and Schimpff recognized that the center needed an ongoing source of operational funding and an endowment. These would be essential for long term growth and effectiveness and the critical first steps to developing the type of statewide advocacy that Shock Trauma enjoyed.

The beginnings of an endowment were met by Greenebaum and his wife. A few years after he became board chair, Greenebaum asked at the beginning of a meeting if board members would stay for a few minutes at the end; so that he could make an announcement. Everyone wondered what the announcement might be: Was he planning to step down? When the time came he stated that it had been exactly five years since his wife, Marlene, had developed and been treated for breast cancer, and that during the bleakest moments he had promised her that everything would go well and that on the fifth anniversary they would make a major commitment. She, indeed, was well with no evidence of disease. Hence today he was announcing that he and Marlene would donate $10 million. He and Marlene wanted the gift to become a permanent endowment of the cancer center. The school and UMMS decided that it would be henceforth known as the University of Maryland Marlene and Stewart Greenebaum Cancer Center.

Over the years the medical system had invested about a million dollars per year into the laboratory research activities of the cancer center in order to maintain their viability. But this would obviously be subject to the ongoing financial status of the medical system and could not be

guaranteed. Once the status of the center was clear after Wilson decided
on the organizational structure, Rapoport decided the cancer center definitely needed an outside funding stream to assure stability and to allow
program development. He began to have talks with the governor, the
governor's assistants and key legislators. He recommended that there be
$5 million placed into the state's operating budget for the cancer center
each year. In essence, he got no support for this idea from Gov. Schaefer
and legislative leaders but was given $5 million in one-time extra capital
funds for the Gudelsky Building to complete the bone marrow transplant
unit construction.

Still feeling the need for an ongoing commitment, he told Schimpff
one day that by asking for $5 million he was not asking for enough and
therefore not getting people's attention. "So let's go back this time and
ask for $10 million per year."

Eventually there was a meeting with Governor Parris N. Glendening
along with Howard "Pete" Rawlings, chairman of the house appropriations committee, and Barbara Hoffman, chair of the senate finance committee—both on the medical system board of directors by reason of their
legislative position. The governor arrived late and soon was reminded by
his secretary that he had another group waiting elsewhere. He listened as
Schimpff made a presentation and then stood up to leave. But Rawlings
asked if he could "have just a minute." The governor, clearly understanding Rawlings' position of power in the legislature, sat back down. Rawlings suggested to the governor that although he would undoubtedly be
remembered as "the education governor" because of his commitment to
educational programs throughout the state during his term in office, he
could also be remembered as the "cancer governor" by the simple act of
committing to significant funding for the cancer center. The governor
listened but made no commitments at that time. A few months later
came a settlement of the tobacco restitution dollars with each involved
state receiving funding based upon a formula agreed to with the tobacco
companies. Maryland was to receive about $100 million per year. The
governor called Rapoport and indicated that he wanted to make a public
announcement about the tobacco restitution dollars and could he do it

at the medical center auditorium? At that session he indicated that he planned to propose to the legislature that the cancer center receive $15 million per year for the coming 10 years, with other funds going to the Johns Hopkins Oncology Center, the health department and a sizable amount to be used for Medicaid funding. In a private conversation with Rapoport and Schimpff, he indicated that he was also committed to the work that Robert Gallo, MD, was doing in the institute of human virology at the university, and he would appreciate a portion of these funds going to Gallo for his work related to viral carcinogenesis. Furthermore, $2 million of the $15 million was to go for a special Baltimore City program in cancer prevention and detection. Johns Hopkins would be receiving an equal sum of money for the same purpose, and the two institutions were to work with the city health department and the state department of health and mental hygiene to develop that program. Finally he agreed with a proposal from Greenebaum that there was to be a statewide outreach program funded with $3 million from the $15 million. It was the addition of these two latter programs that caused him to offer $15 million per year rather than the original $10 million that had been requested some months before for the cancer center.

Although this was the governor's proposal, it had to work its way through the legislature where it was changed but only modestly. The medical system was to receive the $15 million per year for 10 years for the cancer center, which included the $2 million for the city program and $3 million for the outreach program. The dean and the university president were not pleased. Fundamentally, they felt that the monies should have either gone directly to the university or shared between the medical system and the university. The medical center leadership suggested that an oversight group be formed consisting of the president and the dean along with Rapoport and Schimpff. This group would review all recommendations from the center director for use of funds, and all expenditures would have to be based on consensus among the group of four individuals. It was also agreed that the name of the center should always include the words "University of Maryland" before "Marlene and Stewart Greenebaum Cancer Center." This arrangement went a long way to creating better alignment and accord around the cancer center. But all was not contentment because there were real differences on how the outreach monies should be expended. Wilson had some clear ideas on this and had an individual he wished to have lead that program; the medical system essentially accepted his advice but with misgivings that it would not be equivalent to what had been envisioned initially.

The group created around the tobacco restitution funds was not the only attempt to find alignment between the school and the medical system. For many years, the dean and the vice dean (Calia) and the CEOs of the medical system and the medical center met every Wednesday for breakfast. Calia dubbed the group the *Gang of Four*, ever cognizant that the original such *Gang* had died in a contrived airplane crash in China. But the time together was valuable and allowed for the expression of either satisfaction or dissatisfaction over activities and events. A basic principle laid down was that if either party fundamentally disagreed with an approach, the other side would accept that, and the plan would not move forward. It also created a "safe" environment for anyone to express general or specific dissatisfaction with the other party. To some degree, Calia and Schimpff were unofficially charged to be sure the real feelings were addressed, while assuring that the tenor and tone remained cordial and respectful. Among other approaches, the four would always meet with candidates for chairmanship positions as a group. This meant that a "message" was sent to the candidate that the school and hospital were in alignment, and that the two institutions were working together to build new programs. It also meant that during negotiations with a candidate, it was impossible for the candidate to play one side against the other.

LESSONS LEARNED:

First, it is critical to engage the physicians in the planning process and encourage them to participate through a transparent process that ensures them of appropriate input. Developing the new mission and vision, the strategic plan for the future, the technology needs analysis, the capital plan and the master facilities plan were all elements in alignment with the faculty physicians and the school of medicine. Although never so stated, improvements in the medical system were designed with the physicians' input and so were aimed at their and the school's advancement as well.

Second, the changing nature of how patients with acute or chronic diseases must receive the best possible care creates major tensions in the current approaches of medical school and hospital organizational structure and function. It is the disease versus discipline tension that many academic medical centers are grappling with today. Shock Trauma was such an example, and its resolution took time—time for new leaders to emerge and for them to interact and find an accommodation agreeable to all. Cancer was a second one that had to be addressed in order for its success as a patient care project and as a major research endeavor to be possible. Only once the structural issues were resolved was it possible to then address the long term funding issues with the start of an endowment and operational funding from the state tobacco restitution monies.

CHAPTER EIGHT

The Multi-Hospital Vision Unfolds— Adulthood

The medical system began in 1984 as University Hospital, Shock Trauma, and the cancer center. As it turned out, it became a multi-hospital system rather quickly. A tertiary care hospital as part of an academic medical center depends on its faculty physicians to implement leading-edge programs to which community physicians will refer. But it also needs a good plan in place to attract patients to its programs and a method for discharge of those patients that need ongoing care. In short, the hospital needs an effective vertical strategy to assure proper placement of patients for rehabilitation and chronic care, and it needs an effective broad-based horizontal strategy for attracting patients.

Rehabilitation and Orthopedics—the Post Acute Care Vision

Shock Trauma desperately needed an effective institution for rehabilitation care following the acute trauma care of its patients. This led to the establishment of a post-acute-care program at Montebello State Hospital in northeast Baltimore. Montebello originally had been designated as a tuberculosis hospital in 1922 (then named the Sydenham Hospital). The current building had been built in 1957 as the Montebello State Hospital, along with hospitals for chronic care in western Maryland and the eastern shore. But the state's department of health and mental hygiene no longer needed an "old time" tuberculosis hospital for chronic care, and most of the space became available, with some rehabilitation programs beginning in the late 1970s. Initially the state had a contract with the school of medicine to provide medical care at the hospital. Over time, trauma patients became the predominant users. Discussions with the health department secretary, Charles Buck, created a new relationship with the medical system as the contractor. It proved very useful for Shock Trauma patients, and ultimately the medical system was asked to supply a clinical director to manage the trauma patients and the other rehabilitation programs. Flynn became the medical director in the early 1980s. Shortly thereafter the state asked the medical system to manage the hospital under contract, and Flynn became the hospital director/CEO. Montebello was vital to Shock Trauma's success and its vision. It was of great importance to have an effective rehabilitation program for patients who had serious head trauma, spinal cord injury or multiple orthopedic injuries. Further, being able to place the patient in a rehabilitation setting promptly meant that the length of stay within Shock Trauma would be reduced, the cost per patient reduced, and more patients with trauma could be accommodated. This was important because Shock Trauma often had to go on "fly by" meaning that Shock Trauma was full, and the traumatized patient being flown in by helicopter would be diverted to one of the regional level 2 trauma centers rather than coming to Maryland's level 1 Shock Trauma. State legislators, among others, did not like to hear about "fly bys;" so they were prepared to help fund Montebello's rehabilitation program, especially for those trauma patients who could not otherwise afford the care or were not insured for rehabilitation care.

About that same time in the early 1980s, the department of neurology and the department of physical medicine merged into one. Neurology needed a location for referral of its patients, especially those with strokes, who needed rehabilitation care. So the physician staff at Montebello quickly included faculty from neurology/physical medicine and from Shock Trauma. In retrospect, the development of the program at Montebello was the beginning of "vertical integration" by the medical system. Now the medical system was not just an acute care hospital but a true system with a place for the referral of its patients that needed rehabilitation.

In 1990, Flynn became the interim director of MIEMSS after Cowley's retirement. James Ross, who had an earlier administrative experience at Shock Trauma but was now vice president of a large community hospital in Lancaster County, Pa., was recruited to be the new Montebello CEO. Meanwhile the medical system and state officials agreed that Montebello needed to be rebuilt for modern rehabilitation care. An older hospital designed for tuberculosis patients was simply not ideal. The state planned to gift the land and building to the medical system and then financially assist in building the new hospital.

Meanwhile, in 1986, the James Lawrence Kernan Hospital Board decided that it needed to seek an affiliation with a larger hospital. Kernan had been established in 1895 as a children's orthopedic hospital. In 1911 it moved from downtown Baltimore to the 87-acre Radnor estate and took the James Lawrence Kernan name. Initially the mansion house served as the hospital, but over time a new hospital was built with multiple additions. In the 1940s and 1950s it served as a major polio hospital, but that clinical need obviously disappeared rapidly after the introduction of the polio vaccines. Kernan then began to treat adults with orthopedic problems as well, developing an academic affiliation with the school of medicine.

With the advent of arthroscopy and less invasive surgical procedures Kernan Hospital found its inpatient volumes dropping precipitously although the total number of surgical procedures remained constant. But the hospital could not sustain itself without the former level of inpatient admissions. As a result, the Kernan board of trustees began to look for a partner. Kenneth Johnson, MD, chair of neurology and physical medicine, urged Rapoport to respond to Kernan's dilemma. After interviewing multiple hospitals, they chose to affiliate with the newly formed University of Maryland Medical System, in part because of the ongoing relationship with the School. In addition to UMMS management, key individuals to the merger process included Gunther, the board chairman, and Charles Reeves, chairman of the Kernan board. For the medical system the Kernan acquisition was in part a land acquisition opportunity—considered a land bank for future expansion—as well as access to an endowment. The Kernan endowment at the time was valued at about $12 million. The agreement was that the endowment would remain independent of the medical system, but that it could be used only for the benefit of Kernan Hospital. And indeed, over the ensuing years, the endowment board consistently made the earnings from the endowment available for covering operating losses in the early years and then applied it to capital needs such as new technology. Later the endowment board would agree first to back a bond offering for the new rehabilitation wing and later to fund the new chair of orthopedics in the medical school.

For the medical system, Kernan presented a different type of management issue in that University Hospital and Montebello were staffed entirely by faculty physicians whereas Kernan Hospital was staffed by community physicians in private practice in addition to some academic physicians from the school. Clearly, it was important to maintain the desire of the community physicians to practice at Kernan while also enhancing the opportunities for the academic staff. But working the town and gown cultures in the same institution, especially a small institution, was problematic although certainly not insurmountable. This was another situation where working on alignment was very important to all parties.

Again, in retrospect, the acquisition of Kernan was not just a land acquisition in an important part of Baltimore nor was it just the acquisition of a valuable endowment. It was the first step in horizontal integration. Here was an acute care hospital, albeit focused largely on orthopedics, added to the medical system with its ability to refer as appropriate tertiary patients to University Hospital. So the combination of Montebello to serve as a site for sending patients who needed rehabilitation and Kernan for acute care was the beginning of a network development that today has blossomed across the state.

In determining the best approach to helping Kernan not just survive but thrive, an invaluable opportunity emerged. Rather than ask the state to just build a new building on the Montebello grounds, it was decided by the medical system leadership instead to ask the state to help build a completely new rehabilitation hospital on the grounds of Kernan. This would satisfy the state's obligation toward the indigent patients emerging from Shock Trauma and the medical system's need to have rehabilitation opportunities for all of its patients. At the same time it would create synergies with Kernan's long-standing orthopedic programs. In short order, the governor and legislature agreed to provide about half of the $35 million construction cost for a new 128-bed rehabilitation hospital—the largest in the state. With the Kernan endowment pledged as credit, a bond offering through Kernan Hospital met the other half of the capital cost. The state also agreed to continue its operating allowance toward the care of the indigent Shock Trauma patients as it had done at Montebello. At the same time that the new rehabilitation hospital was opened in 1996, major renovations within the current Kernan Hospital were completed to upgrade the orthopedic program with new operating rooms, a new intensive care unit and revamped patient care rooms. In short, Kernan Hospital had been completely revitalized in less than a decade. Ross became the CEO of the combined institutions and went through the process of merging not just the hospitals but the widely different cultures that had developed over the better part of a century at each institution.

An integral part of the entire rehabilitation program for the medical system was to create a rehabilitation network. This was organized by Donald Joyce, who was recruited from a for-profit rehabilitation hospital chain. Over time, outpatient physical therapy and rehabilitation facilities were created to the north, northwest, west, southwest and at Shipley's Choice in the southeast. This meant that patients "graduating" from the rehabilitation hospital could get their continuing outpatient therapy in their local community while still under medical system staff supervision. At the same time these outpatient facilities could serve other elements of the community, which in turn created referrals back to the new rehabilitation hospital. To this network was added a home health care agency and other elements that created a full system of care for the patient who needed rehabilitation.

Looking back, four elements characterized the Kernan and Montebello strategy. First, the medical system acquired Kernan as a growth opportunity. Second, it forged a vision for a strong orthopedics service that incorporated both community and faculty physicians. Indeed, Kernan had and still has the potential to be a regional and even national orthopedic referral center. Third, Montebello was redeveloped into the state's outstanding rehabilitation hospital. And fourth, the system created a setting where Shock Trauma could refer its patients needing rehabilitation and thus improve patient care while freeing beds for new admissions.

Chronic and Long-Term Care

Just as Montebello Hospital and then Kernan having assisted Shock Trauma and the department of neurology with rapidly moving patients into a good rehabilitation setting, the medical system also needed to get patients into a longer-term care setting, such as patients who needed to be on respirators for prolonged periods. The Christ Lutheran Church downtown had created Deaton, a combined long-term care facility and nursing home on its adjacent property. A total of 370 beds (180 for chronic care and 190 for long-term care) were located at the inner harbor next door to the Harbor Court Hotel, an ideal location close by the medical center. It would create a "back door" from the medical center for neurology patients, pulmonary care patients and general medicine patients, among others. The church elders had decided that they were no longer equipped to manage such a large facility given the changes in health care reimbursement and other issues. They proposed to sell Deaton, and after lengthy negotiations the medical system purchased it for $12 million.

Primary Care Strategy—One Key to Tertiary Care Referrals to UMMC

The medical system now had a working pre-hospital network in Express Care and an effective post-hospital-care system with the combination of Kernan/Montebello, Deaton, the outpatient rehabilitation/physical therapy centers and the home health care agency. It was an effective vertical strategy. But the medical system needed to look for ways to encourage referral of tertiary care patients to its flagship academic hospital—a horizontal strategy. Patients are referred by physicians, but physicians tend to have close affiliations with one or more community hospitals. The medical system therefore began looking to community hospitals for affiliation or merger arrangements that would help ensure an increasing flow of tertiary patients. After on-again, off-again conversations, Sabatini convinced the CEO of Maryland General Hospital and Health System along with one of its key board members to initiate serious dialogue about an affiliation. Rapoport sent Ashworth to see the hospital's CEO, J. R. Wood. "Tell him to do something 'bold'" said Rapoport.

Ashworth returned and said, "JR is ready to be 'bold;' so let's move ahead."

Maryland General had a long and storied history as an outstanding hospital, with an excellent medical staff and a strong residency program. Like many community hospitals it had once had a school of nursing but had closed it a few decades before. It was next to a major state office facility at the northern end of the business district of Howard Street. This location had traditionally been the "5th Avenue" of Baltimore with its four major department stores and the smaller boutique stores that clustered near them. But the department stores were now gone, and Howard Street had come on hard times. The hospital likewise had lost most of its former well-heeled patients and no longer had as large a medical staff. But it was a busy, full-service general hospital that catered largely to those living in western and central Baltimore. Twenty years before, Maryland General, like many inner city hospitals, had planned to move to the suburbs, already having purchased land to the north in mid-central Baltimore County. But Mayor Schaefer saw Maryland General as one of the anchors of northern Howard Street and was loathe to having it leave the city. He lobbied hard to prevent the move. The hospital stayed but over time became largely populated with patients on Medicare and Medicaid, admitting relatively few with private insurance such as Blue Cross. Maryland General needed a major capital infusion for a face-lift and ultimately for a new hospital building. This combination of circumstances led Maryland General to the affiliation with the medical system.

The addition of MGH was the start of a true horizontal strategy for the medical system. Until then most of the activity had been to develop the vertical strategy with Montebello, Deaton, the home health agency, and the physical therapy sites and to some degree the acquisition of Kernan, although it was in fact an acute care hospital.

After the merger the management team realized that although Kernan, Deaton and Maryland General each had a chief executive officer, the academic flagship did not. Key board leaders agreed that there should be a corporate staff led by Rapoport in a new off-site corporate office and that Schimpff should no longer be chief operating officer of the medical system but rather chief executive officer of what would now be known as the University of Maryland Medical Center.

Cementing Referrals from the Suburban Communities

When the outpatient facility was built at Shipley's Choice by the Medical System, it created a collaborative approach with Anne Arundel Health System based in Annapolis. Sabatini along with Schimpff suggested to the chief executive of the Anne Arundel Health System that they consider an affiliation or merger with the medical system. This was considered, but instead the Anne Arundel Health System leadership and board members decided that it was appropriate to first consider a merger with North Arundel Hospital. The county, with a population as large as Baltimore City with its 10 hospitals, had but two hospitals. They generally divided the county into north and south and had relatively little competition from other hospitals. The two institutions got into serious discussions but eventually parted company. North Arundel then considered a merger with Mercy Hospital but again this did not come to fruition. Soon, North Arundel's chief executive, James Walker, contacted the medical system, and serious negotiations began promptly. In short order North Arundel Hospital, along with its relatively new acquisition, Mt. Washington Pediatric Hospital, joined the medical system. For North Arundel, access to capital was a key consideration. North Arundel Hospital had a large and successful cardiac care program, indeed representing about 20% of its admissions. But it had a limited cancer care program and did not have an obstetrics unit. It had just finished building a new emergency room which eventually became the largest in the state based on annual visits. The northern part of Anne Arundel County was rapidly growing, especially around the Baltimore-Washington International Airport. There was every reason to believe that North Arundel Hospital could and would grow with the right plans, adequate capital and access to the medical center/school of medicine faculty and staff. From the medical center's perspective, the cardiac program was critical. Working effectively with the cardiologists at North Arundel Hospital would assure that their patients would be referred to the medical center for angioplasty, electrophysiology procedures and cardiac surgery. At the same time, assisting in the development of their cancer program would open opportunities for the University of Maryland Greenebaum Cancer Center to extend its outreach programs. Finally, since there was no obstetrics program at North Arundel, developing it could be a major opportunity for the obstetrics program at the medical center and especially the faculty physicians.

Mt. Washington Pediatric Hospital is a unique institution which offers long-term and chronic care for infants and young children, usually those born prematurely who have pulmonary dysfunction or other difficult medical problems. Over the years about half of its patients came from the neonatal intensive care unit of the Medical Center and the other half from Johns Hopkins. It was important in the course of the merger to assure that the Hopkins patients would be appropriately accepted and serviced, and that the Hopkins faculty physicians who worked at Mt. Washington Pediatric Hospital would find the circumstances comfortable into the future. This was done, but some years later an agreement was reached with Johns Hopkins to have joint ownership and management of this institution, thereby cementing the relationship and the combined needs of all parties.

LESSONS LEARNED:

A tertiary care hospital as part of an academic medical center depends on its faculty physicians to implement leading-edge programs to which

community physicians will refer. But the medical center also needs an
effective vertical strategy to assure proper placement of patients for rehabilitation and chronic care, and it needs an effective horizontal strategy
which in the medical system's case has been a combination of community hospitals, the placement of the emergency medicine program at ten
of Maryland's hospitals and the development of the Express Care system
for rapid, effective communication and transport of critically ill patients
to the medical center. In addition, the medical system is the beneficiary
of the statewide program of trauma care that has its pinnacle at Shock
Trauma.

The University of Maryland Medical Center—The System's Flagship

As the medical system grew, the original base of University Hospital needed its own fully-committed local governance and management team. The University of Maryland Medical Center, as it was now named, also needed an internal culture where all staff and physicians felt welcome, encouraged and valued. Creating the culture helped assure a return to profitability. Concurrently, an intense focus on both new technology and faculty-led clinical research served as strong marketing avenues.

Frank Bramble replaced Greenebaum as board chairman in January 1999. Bramble had been CEO at Maryland National Bank, and after it was acquired by Nations Bank (later Bank of America), he became chief executive officer and later chairman of the board of the First National Bank of Maryland (which later became AllFirst Bank). When he took over as chairman, the medical system had just gone through a difficult financial downturn. A trio of events had caused the medical center to lose money. Most important was that the HSCRC did not fully fund inflation for a few years because Medicare was pushing down payments; so the commission had to "put the brakes" on inflation adjustments to Maryland hospitals. So despite medical cost inflation, rates did not increase. A second important factor was Maryland's decision to shift Medicaid from fee for service to managed care. In the process it reduced Medicaid payments by about 20% and about 20% of what was left went to fund the managed care entities that held the risk. As a result only about 60% of the dollars previously available remained for direct care of patients. Finally commercial insurers had for a number of years in the mid 1990s kept premiums low so as to increase market share. But as medical costs inflated they were caught short and needed to find ways to rapidly ratchet down their expenses. They did this by delaying payments, by finding technical issues that could justify sending a bill back for additional data or by outright denial of payments on various grounds. The combination of these three factors led to a sharp drop in revenues and in cash collections for all hospitals in Maryland, but impacted the teaching hospitals with large Medicaid populations the greatest. The medical system had been pleased to slowly but surely develop a $100 million cash position; this helped to increase the bond rating and was thought to be a good message when mergers and acquisitions were considered. But the reduction in revenues and the slowdown in cash collections forced a drawdown of cash reserves. The phase III capital plan, with its signature Weinberg Building, had to be delayed. Initially all non-clinical hiring at the former University Hospital was suspended, but by late fall it became necessary to have a 200-person layoff and a further cut in expenditures. By the end of the fiscal year the medical system had negative net income of $17 million, a remarkable change of fortune from just the year before, which had been the best year ever with $27 million net income.

Six months later, when Bramble assumed the chairmanship, the management team presented a financial plan to him that had four elements: continued cost containment; an aggressive plan to grow additional admissions plus clinic visits and procedures such as cardiac catheterizations; a plan to improve cash collections with a newly recruited successful team; and, lastly, the medical system was working closely with the HSCRC to enhance rates. At this same time, Maryland General Hospital came into the medical system. This acquisition emphasized the need to create the University of Maryland Medical Center as a separate entity within the Medical System. The University Hospital/Shock Trauma/Greenebaum Cancer Center had been the medical system, until Montebello, Kernan, and Deaton were added. But with the addition of Maryland General Hospital, the medical system was indeed a true system of acute care hospitals plus post acute care facilities. A separate dedicated management team was needed for the overall medical system and another one for the system's academic flagship hospital, which would now be known as the University of Maryland Medical Center. The board approved the financial action plan which was essentially for the University of Maryland Medical Center and encouraged the new organizational structure.

Rapoport appointed Schimpff as chief executive officer of the University of Maryland Medical Center and Ashworth as the chief operating officer. They and the other senior leaders (Franey as senior vice president and CFO; Alison Brown as senior vice president for business development; McCullough as senior vice president for patient care services; David Rorison, MD, MBA, as senior vice president and chief medical officer; and later Michael Minear as senior vice president and chief information officer for both UMMC and the medical system overall) recognized that the financial action plan's success was absolutely critical, and that an institutional turnaround had to occur rapidly. But there was another issue. The financial downturn had laid bare some cultural issues that had not been adequately dealt with in the past. The medical center was full of good and well-intentioned individuals, many of whom had been state employees, yet they still did not fully understand what was expected in an enterprise environment. So the culture change issue was to transform these individuals and the systems at the same time in a way that was effective yet appropriate. This was difficult given the financial downturn and a major layoff. Anxieties were high. The culture change of the previous years toward a relentless focus on finance had been effective, yet it had precluded an adequate focus on quality and safety, graduate medical education and other issues of importance in an academic medical center.

Culture Change

A new director of organizational development in the human resources department, Elizabeth Hostetler, PhD, recommended a specific approach to improve the culture of the organization. She presented compelling data that, in for-profit corporations, when the staff had a clear concept of the organization's strategy and vision, felt a sense of involvement, and believed there was organizational consistency and adaptability, then the net income would be substantially higher than that of organizations that scored lower on this validated survey. The medical center encouraged her to survey the staff using this product. The result, to all the senior managers' chagrin, was exceptionally low scores. Of particular concern was that the middle managers' scores were much lower than the general staff and the senior managers. This led to a concerted effort over a four-year period to improve the institutional culture, focusing first on middle managers and then on the entire staff.

The reasons for the effort were clear. Success in managing and leading an academic hospital is considered high stakes—ultimately people's lives depend on effective, proper decision-making. But medical centers are highly complex institutions with multiple "products"—surgery, medicine and pediatrics, along with residency training programs and medical student education—and they serve as the venue for much medical research by the faculty. They boast many specialty areas, from cardiac surgery and kidney transplant to normal childbirth and well-baby care, and conflicting expectations are involved, such as cost controls counterbalanced by the highest quality care possible. Health care today is turbulent and fast changing. The end product "matters." A hospital is unique in that those with the power to consume resources, namely the physicians, are generally not employees of the organization (the only such industry of which we know). This anomalous structure demands the development of effective partnerships—alignment—unlike any other industry. This was the critical need at the University of Maryland Medical Center.

Part of the culture change that also needed to occur was to be certain that all of the staff were working toward the same goals and felt mutually supported. Part of the cost reduction approaches in earlier years had effectively reorganized one function but had failed to create the needed supports to assure that the second function could handle the changes. For example, changes to nursing to make costs more variable and less fixed were effective, but it meant that nursing was much more dependent upon other services such as transportation and pharmacy—no longer could nurses be expected to push patients to radiology or go to the pharmacy to pick up medications. We learned by experience that we had not fully planned for these needs, putting greater stress on the nurses until corrected by assuring good alignment among all of the hospital functions.

This was also a time when unions were attempting to organize housekeeping and dietary staff. Given the recent downturn and the cost reduction approaches, it was a good time for the unions to consider organizing. As it turned out, the culture changes were effective in convincing staff that they did not need or want the union, and a vote was never requested.

The goals of a not-for-profit hospital, like any not-for-profit business, are mission based, not profit based. Yet, the hospital must be financially successful if it is to reinvest in plant and equipment and be able to attract and retain the best and brightest to care for patients, teach and conduct research. "No money, no mission" is an apt term. In this setting, leadership must set the course for the future, make prudent decisions on resource utilization and inspire the physicians, along with the professional and nonprofessional staff, to be willing participants in an ongoing yet complex and difficult journey. As it turned out, over a four-year time horizon the culture changed and with it, the bottom line. A series of organizational developmental interventions were instituted to assist the management to manage but also to lead; to inform and to listen to all staff members; to lay out a clear, yet simple vision of the future; to publish and adhere to a strategic plan and an annual operating plan; and to maximize the value of the diverse workforce. Through the Denison Culture Survey, changes were measured at the unit level annually, from 1999 to 2004. The results showed substantial increases in scores, which correlated well to increases in the bottom line (FIG 9-1). To be clear, the medical center benefitted mightily from effective bargaining with the Commission for higher rates, and collections that were augmented by the newly recruited team. The culture survey scores increased dramatically across all traits, and all levels, during a multi-year period. The steps taken to lead the medical center out of a period of profound financial and emotional distress led to a positive state, one with enthusiasm for the present and hope for the future. It became clear that managers under stress needed to know how to take charge of what was changing and what was staying the same, and address each differently. Bringing these culture change initiatives together assisted UMMC to achieve the goals of the financial plan, allowing the institution to reinvest in the critical plant and technologies essential to the future of the business.

FIG 9-1

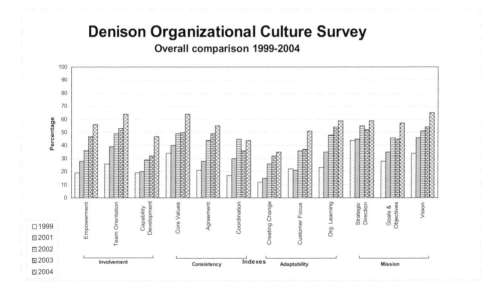

Graduate Medical Education

Another important issue was graduate medical education (GME). It is an inherent function of any academic medical center hospital, but there had been so much to do, so little time and so little money at the time of the medical system's creation in 1984 that a truly intensive approach to GME had not been possible. Partly as a result, the school of medicine sought control of this function in the early 1990s, claiming it as part of its education mission. Tension reigned for a while, and then the medical system agreed to have the school of medicine essentially manage the

GME function although the medical system would maintain the financial, contracting and other fiduciary responsibilities. At some point in
time the school of medicine realized that an outside review might not go
well and abruptly turned the program back to the medical center. The
medical center was just then reorganizing as a separate entity within the
medical system, and in the process recruited a vice president for medical
affairs and a director for graduate medical education. They re-energized
the program, developed systems, improved accountability and brought
the credentialing process under a centralized entity. All this was done
while encouraging the individual departments to manage the educational content of their GME programs while working with the school of
medicine and an oversight committee to address the critical elements of
a training program.

A few years before, Schimpff had been called about 5 p.m. one afternoon by a reporter for the *Sunpapers* who indicated that he had written
a story about an unlicensed physician among the residents. His article
would appear in the next day's newspaper, and he was requesting a comment. As it turned out, he had been working on this story for some
months. The background was as follows. A physician had applied for
a special training program in Shock Trauma. Generally, a resident in
training does not need a medical license. But since this program was not
part of the national graduate medical education certified programs, but
rather a specialized program in trauma surgery, it required that any such
individual have a medical license. When he was accepted he received
a letter indicating that it was an acceptance pending receipt of proof of
graduation from an accredited medical school, certification that he had
completed an approved surgical training program and that he had a valid
medical license. When he arrived, a secretary in Shock Trauma asked
him for his medical license. He responded that he had just moved from
Ohio, and that it was in his safe deposit box near his Ohio residence
where his family still lived. He would be going back in a few weeks and
would pick it up and bring it to her. This response seemed reasonable
to the secretary; so she waited a few weeks and then asked him again
for the license. He responded that he had forgotten to pick it up, but

he would be going back home again shortly and would certainly do so. This went on for a number of cycles until she told her supervisor. He in turn told the clinical director of Shock Trauma who commented that the individual to date had proven himself as a competent surgeon. No action was taken other than to send word back that he again should be asked to procure his proof of licensure.

By the time the phone call came it was November, five months after his arrival. It turned out that he had graduated from medical school with the condition that he pass his medical licensure examination. He had failed, and hence his diploma was not valid. He had completed a surgical residency because no one had checked on the status of his medical school diploma. Now, he was taking a post residency training program and had failed to produce a license because, indeed, he was unlicensed. The *Baltimore Sun* appropriately chastised the medical center for not having a definitive system to verify the physician's status. Up to this time, residency details were handled by the individual departments. They interviewed and chose individuals for the residency programs; they were responsible for checking issues such as medical school graduation and, where appropriate, prior residency status. It quickly became apparent that the medical center needed to centralize these functions just as it did with the attending faculty staff. Although it created a substantial increase in expenditures, this change assured that every individual among the almost 1,000 residents and fellows in training was indeed appropriately credentialed. It meant contacting each accepted applicant's medical school for primary verification of their graduation (not accepting a copy of the diploma) and contacting each and every program that the individual had trained in previously to obtain a signed letter from the training program director that the individual had performed satisfactorily. Further, the medical center would check for malpractice claims and any issues of drug or alcohol abuse, major legal issues, etc. These were important and necessary policy changes that helped to ensure a first-class group of physicians in training.

Use the Truth to Make Improvements

When I was told by the director of public affairs that a reporter had called asking for a comment on an unlicensed physician my first reaction was "that can't be, not here."

It was about 5:45 p.m. and of course many staff had left for the day. We quickly found out who the physician was and learned from the reporter that he had been working on the story for some months. I wondered why he felt it was OK to call now for a comment before the paper went to press rather than call a few days or even weeks ago to tell us of his findings. But that was not the way the system worked, and I knew it. We could not reach the doctor but did send a messenger to his home with a letter stating that he was fired unless he could immediately prove that he was indeed licensed. But the horse was out of the barn. Not a happy situation but the need was for us to accept that we just did not have good systems in place, and that we needed to fix them—now. Sometimes reality, if accepted, surely can make the place better.

-Stephen C. Schimpff, MD

Medical Center Governance

The medical center was established in 1999 essentially as a separate hospital among the six hospitals in the University of Maryland Medical System. It now had its own senior management team but did not have a board of directors. Although it was a subsidiary of the medical system, it did not have legal standing in a technical sense as did Maryland General or North Arundel hospitals. Nevertheless, it was decided to establish a committee that would serve as the equivalent of a board of directors of the medical center. This was made up of members of the parent UMMS board, and they met, initially, on a bi-monthly basis immediately following the medical system board meetings. There was now a new chairman of the board, John Erickson, who agreed to serve as the chair of the medical center committee for the first year. Thereafter Bramble, the previous UMMS board chairman, served as the UMMC committee chair for about two years. The creation of the committee (or board) was a particularly valuable function. It gave the senior management team a

board of directors to both challenge them and at the same time advocate
for the medical center within the parent board of the medical system,
just as each of the other hospital boards had its delegates seated at the
parent board.

The medical center committee/board worked with management to
develop a strategic plan for the medical center. The mission "to heal, to
teach, to discover" was reiterated as was the vision to be a "standard-setting academic medical center." Given the mission and vision, the strategic plan dictated that the medical center would focus not only on patient care but would appropriately focus on graduate medical education
and on assisting the medical staff to conduct clinical research within the
hospital. The medical school applied for and was granted a general clinical research center (GCRC) which was created via a major renovation
to the 12th floor of the south hospital building. Most importantly the
message went out to all of management and staff that the medical center
recognized the importance of education, training and research as an integral part of its mission. Indeed, the strategic plan dictated that growth
in the future would be based upon marketing the research discoveries of
the clinical faculty. Henceforth clinical program development funding
would go preferentially to those programs with the greatest promise for
new approaches to treat or cure diseases and would thereby generate
referrals to the medical center. Restated, it was recognized that the principal mechanism to recruit patients to the medical center from outside
of the city for tertiary and quaternary care was to emphasize the new approaches that the faculty physicians were constantly developing.

Meanwhile the financial plan with its four elements of cost containment, volume growth, enhancing rates from the commission and improving cash collections was effective. Each year the medical center's
net income improved resulting in as much as $42 million by the end of
the fourth year. Net revenue continued to climb for two reasons. Rates
were continually enhanced, and admissions, along with the numbers of
procedures and surgeries, climbed dramatically as a result of the new
facilities and technologies that had been brought to bear in recent years.
Most advantageous was the opening of first the Gudelsky Building, then

the Weinberg Building and the development of many clinical programs in cardiac care, neuro care, cancer care, etc.

The Importance of Teams in Construction of New Buildings

With the financial downturn from 1997 to 1999, the next major recapitalization project—the Weinberg Building—had been put on hold. At that time the land had been acquired, the old buildings razed and a bond issued for part of the construction. But construction also required strong cash flow. With no activity for two plus years, inflation eroded the contingency allocation but even more importantly several members of the architectural, construction, and in-house teams were no longer in place. Once work began again, new team members were without the project history, compromising speed and efficiency. Although it was necessary to halt the project at the time, it would—in retrospect—have been advisable to do more to ensure that the various teams with their institutional knowledge stayed intact.

A Patient Safety Wakeup Call

A tiny premature infant was in the neonatal intensive care unit with the very best of doctors and nurses, all well trained and very experienced. The baby was on a ventilator, had an intravenous line in place and was being fed through a feeding tube. At about 5:00 a.m., in the morning the nurses routinely changed all the various tubing in order to reduce the chance of infection. It is done at this time of day because there is less activity—the parents are home, the doctors are not present and the phones are not ringing. One morning at 6:30 a.m., the monitor indicated that this infant had a rising heart rate. There was no apparent reason, but the pediatricians were summoned and likewise could find no cause. About an hour later someone realized that the baby's feeding tube had been inadvertently switched for the intravenous tube—formula was going directly into the baby's veins! What had happened at 5:00 a.m. to allow this error to occur? The nurse on duty that night had 12 years of experience with premature infants, was highly respected, was a role model for new nurses and had a perfect attendance record. There had been no apparent distractions at the time—

no other emergencies, no phone calls. The nurse was not overloaded with patients and was not "covering" for anyone else who might have left for a break, snack or to run an errand. In essence, everything was fine at that time on her shift; there were no extraneous reasons for the nurse to make this mistake. It was "just" a human error, albeit a serious one.

This episode was a "wake up" call for me on patient safety. I was chief operating officer of the hospital system at the time and was about to become CEO of the flagship academic medical center. A new chair of the board of trustees had just taken over, and he asked to spend time after each board meeting touring the hospital and learning more about patient care. On the first of such tours, we went to the neonatal intensive care unit where the head nurse took us from room to room. The first room had the "growers," medical slang for somewhat premature infants that just needed some time in the hospital before going home. She explained that the baby of President and Mrs. Kennedy 40 years before would have fit into this group. But at present essentially all of these infants survive and live perfectly normal lives. From there we went to each of three rooms with successively smaller infants. At the last room the babies could only be termed "tiny." Indeed it seemed amazing that they could live, even with all of the medical and nursing help available. The chairman, standing by an incubator and looking down at one of these infants, asked if this child could possibly survive.

"Yes," was the nurse's reply. "This baby has no congenital problems; so we will just need to keep up with using the respirator, giving it IV fluids and feeding it through the feeding tube for a few months. Then it should be fine."

I could tell that the board chair was amazed, as was I, and that he really felt good. Here he was volunteering a lot of his time, and now he could have the satisfaction that "his" hospital was doing great things for the citizenry.

Two days later I was called about the premature infant that had the tubes reversed. It was the same infant that we had stood near and talked about on the tour. I knew I had to call the chairman, but I dreaded doing so; it would be a real "downer" for him. And how could I explain that it was "just a mistake," terrible, but a mistake nonetheless? The story con-

tinues, but I would like you to know that it served as a personal "wake up" call for me. I thought we paid attention to safety, but upon reflection and some investigation it became abundantly clear that giving real, intensive, and sustained attention to patient safety is critical for any hospital CEO. Of course we all care about safety and our patients' welfare, but I can state from experience that most of us just do not realize what needs to be done, and done differently to make a real difference in avoiding errors.

-Stephen C. Schimpff, MD

Over time the leadership began to understand the necessity for addressing safety. Unfortunately hospital culture, the medical center included, is not conducive to improved safety. Critical is an open, non judgmental attitude about errors because "to err is human," and the real need is to get each error reported; so it can be appropriately investigated using root cause analysis. This can be followed with changes to processes to prevent a similar error in the future, or to detect it soon enough that it can be remedied before harm occurs. This means a charge from the board of directors to the CEO and management team which then radiates through the entire organization. It means putting the needed tools in place to collect data, analyze it and make corrections. It also means having the needed clinical leadership as well as unit management. And it means having useful technologies that have or are becoming available such as RFID, pharmacy robots and good digital information systems.

The hospital must be accountable and so must each staff member. The patient and the patient's family deserve a straightforward explanation, a sincere apology and prompt monetary compensation. But an error should not mean loss of credentials, firing or humiliation—so often the practice today. What it should mean is an attempt to understand why the error occurred, and what systems the hospital can put in place to prevent its recurrence. In short, it is the institution that is responsible to assist its staff in avoiding errors or to identify them and make corrections in time to avert disaster.

Once a root cause analysis is done, there is often a straightforward step that can help prevent a recurrence. In the case of the IV-feeding tube mix-up in the vignette, a simple solution is to use a feeding tube with a special color to differentiate it from the IV tubing and to use a connector that is triangular rather than round. One is a visual clue and the other a type of "forcing function."

LESSONS LEARNED:

First, the medical center, like the community hospitals, benefitted from having its own board. This brought greater oversight along with advocacy at the system board. Second, any hospital needs an internal culture where all staff and physicians feel welcome, encouraged and valued. Working to achieve the culture was a critical element of the medical center's return to profitability. Third, it was important to recognize and formalize the obvious fact that a tertiary hospital with an affiliated medical school derives enormous benefit from the continual development of new diagnostic and treatment modalities of the faculty's ongoing research activities. Indeed these are the key reasons why many patients choose to come long distances for their care. Fourth, teams are a critical element in effective project development, and it is important to maintain them, if at all possible, during difficult financial times. Fifth, quality care and patient safety must become major areas of focus for the senior leadership of all hospitals including those of academic medical centers. Despite a lack of familiarity with improved methodologies to augment safety and quality, these are subjects board members must also routinely address.

CHAPTER TEN

Fund Raising and Endowment Creation— From Nothing to Something

P rior to 1984, the medical system, like the school, had never engaged in serious fund raising. As a state owned entity, the university and its hospital leadership had not assigned development much importance over the years. But as a separate not-for-profit corporation, development would be essential to recapitalizing the medical system. Basically, the system was starting from zero. It had the phrase "University of Maryland" in its name suggesting to many that it did not need contributed funds. There was a powerhouse at fund raising across town named Johns Hopkins Hospital that had an incredible local and national reputation. The relationship between the medical system and school was problematic. The board, a major source of contributed funds in many charitable organizations, did not have a history of contributing and was not made up of necessarily affluent individuals. But if the medical system was to be successful, it would have to be successful at fund raising as well.

With this background, Rapoport chose to use his personal connections as best he could to begin the process. Friends and colleagues led him to various donors, many in the Jewish and corporate community. The first major gifts came from the Gudelsky family. They never expected care other than that afforded to every other patient; they never indicated their wealth to any of their caregivers. The nurses became very fond of Homer Gudelsky, who always treated them with respect and admiration. One day, Schimpff, then cancer center director, was asked to come to the outpatient area for a birthday celebration.

"Whose birthday?" he asked.

"Mr. Gudelsky, and Colleen (the head nurse) has baked him a cake," was the reply.

Such was their affection for him. Gudelsky's initial oncologist, Richard Levitt, MD, was well regarded by the Gudelskys, and they asked him if there was anything he needed for his work. After initially demurring, he indicated that he needed a new microscope; this led to a $5,000 gift and later to a $50,000 gift to purchase further equipment for his laboratory. This was the beginning of their generosity to the medical system.

A few years later the medical system approached the Gudelsky family to help support the purchase of its first magnetic resonance imaging device (MRI). The Gudelskys gave $1 million, dedicating the facility to Anna Gudelsky, Homer's sister. By the late 1980s it was time to begin to build the replacement building. Fund raising would be important for this plan to come to fruition. Rapoport took Schimpff to meet with the Gudelskys and outline the plan for the new building. The family decided to donate $5 million with the understanding that the state would make a major contribution. Rapoport then went to Gov. Schaefer and outlined the project, along with the lead gift from the Gudelskys. Thus was born the public-private partnership for what became known as the Gudelsky Building. But it was also the beginning of serious fund raising for the medical system. Shortly, a campaign was begun to raise $20 million additional dollars toward the building. This effort was successful with lead gifts coming from board members, staff, friends and grateful patients. Importantly, this campaign began a tradition of fund raising. To do so required explaining that, yes, the name of the institution was "University of Maryland Medical System," but that it was a separate not-for-profit corporation. And yes, it was receiving substantial funds from the state for the new building but not nearly enough to complete the job. With time and persistence, potential donors began to recognize the value of the medical system to the community and the need for external gifts.

After completion of the Gudelsky Building in 1994, which was basically a new patient room tower, it became essential that the medical center craft a vision to provide new imaging, interventional radiology, new operating rooms, and new intensive care facilities. This project would ultimately cost almost twice the expenditure of the Gudelsky Tower. Again the funding plan would require state support, additional debt, and a fund raising campaign.

The Weinberg Foundation under the leadership of Bernard Siegel was approached, shortly after its creation for a lead gift in support of the new building. Siegel had received personal health services at the University of Maryland Medical Center; so that he was quite familiar with Rapoport's vision and how the medical center was important overall to Maryland's health care delivery system. Wasserman, formerly chief of staff to Gov. Schaefer and then secretary of the department of economic and business development, joined the leadership team of the medical system and worked closely with Rapoport in gaining approval from the Weinberg Foundation for a $12 million lead gift in support of this project which would ultimately become the Weinberg Building. As it turned out, both Rapoport and Siegel had a shared passion for the redevelopment of the west side of Baltimore and worked together with others and with the city leaders. The result was a furthering of the relationship while making a significant improvement to the quality of life in Baltimore.

Another large gift came with the support of two of Rapoport's high school classmates and close friends, Berger and Ron Creamer, with whom Rapoport had maintained a friendship for over 50 years. Joseph Schwartz was a business partner and friend of Berger and Creamer. They introduced Rapoport to the Schwartz family. Rapoport shared with them his capital vision for the medical system. Schwartz and his wife Corinne had been a very generous family over many years contributing to schools and cultural organizations throughout the country. Over a period of almost 10 years, the Schwartz family became close friends with Rapoport and the medical system. The family gave $1 million for the

The Weinberg Building, 2006

new Schaefer Building at Kernan Hospital, and $5 million toward the Weinberg Building at the medical center. These gifts came over time as Rapoport introduced members of the medical system leadership to the Schwartz family.

Two very key team members included Flynn and his wife Lacy who also became very dear friends of the Schwartz family. Schwartz experienced a stroke in his later years, and Flynn and the team at Kernan provided a vigorous and aggressive physiotherapy program that helped both patient and family cope with this disability. The dedication that Flynn and his wife showed to the Schwartz family was one of many examples of how this couple, as an effective team, extended and committed themselves to patients and families. It is also an example of sincere stewardship making a major difference in fund raising.

Rapoport also introduced the Schwartz family to Stephen Bartlett, MD, who headed the transplant program. Over a period of several years and visits to the Schwartz family home in Florida, Rapoport and Bartlett outlined the plan for transplant services to become a key part of the Weinberg Building. As an outcome, the family requested that their gift be used in part to support the surgical services in the Weinberg Building.

There were other positive outcomes. The personal relationships Rapoport and Wasserman developed with others in the community such as Howard Brown and Willard Hackerman resulted in additional large gifts. And of course the $10 million gift from the Greenebaums led to the naming of the cancer center. The success of the center in its research and care missions helped open the door for the state to commit tobacco restitution funding for a 10-year period, totaling over $100 million. This created multiple "shared resources" for researchers in genomics, proteomics, X-ray refraction and nuclear magnetic resonance imaging, translational research, biostatistics and others. It also allowed for added recruitments of outstanding scientists and clinicians.

In 1991, Ron Shapiro, a prominent Baltimore attorney and agent for many athletes, asked his long time friend Nathan Schnaper, MD, professor of psychiatry and head of psycho-social services for the cancer center, if he could be of help. Schnaper suggested the formation of a board of visitors which would be an advocacy group in the community, a marketing venue for the cancer center and a fund raising group. Shapiro agreed and with Richard Adams (a trust officer) and Mark Kolman (a lawyer and patient of the center cured of his leukemia) selected outstanding individuals to serve. Over the years this board of visitors has been of great value and in the process introduced many individuals to the center and the system. Similar boards were developed, as well, for Shock Trauma and for Maryland's Hospital for Children, each with powerful advocacy and support for fund raising.

Leonard Stoler, a well known auto dealer in the Baltimore region, along with his wife Rosalyn toured the radiation oncology area and learned about the promising new programs in cancer care. It was determined that the Stolers were fascinated by the concept of the multidisciplinary team approach to care as was commonplace in the cancer center. A pressing need was for a new and renovated location for outpatients to be evaluated and treated using this highly coordinated, multidisciplinary team approach.

"Whose Side are You On?"

Greenebaum arranged for Rapoport and me to accompany him to the Stolers' home one afternoon. I was to make the presentation, Rapoport to emphasize the importance of the cancer center and then Greenebaum would make the ask. We first toured the Stoler's beautiful home, built about 100 years earlier, and then sat in their sun porch. We were on one side, Len and Rosalyn sat across from us. The Stolers were gracious and listened carefully, asking many questions about the multi-disciplinary approach to care, and how a new out-patient facility would make a huge difference to patient care. Greenebaum asked for a gift of $5 million.

Stoler then indicated that he and his wife would make a decision and get back to Greenebaum shortly. "Whatever our decision, we will let you know soon."

But before we could say "Thank you and goodbye," Rosalyn said "Len, we just have to help these people; the patients need our help."

He looked at her with a smile and said "Which side of the room are you sitting on?"

Within a few weeks, they sent word of a $5 million gift to fund the Rosalyn and Leonard Stoler Pavilion for the cancer center.

-Stephen C. Schimpff, MD

These gifts from private individuals and tobacco restitution funds from the state allowed the center to apply to the NCI for formal designation, an accomplishment which was granted in 2008.

Large gifts of this nature were important, very important, but it was also necessary to establish an organized development program. To this end, the medical system recruited staff and leadership. For a time, it was done jointly with the school of medicine, sharing the costs and allocating the income based on donor preference. But the arrangement was never comfortable between the two parties, and neither felt the one was fully committed to the other's needs. Eventually, the dean decided to forge his own development program, feeling that he could do better for the school that way, probably encouraged at least in part by his university president. The two entities continued separate fund raising, but the leaders and the staffs simply did not work well together. The dean did not want the physicians actively assisting the medical system, feeling that their loyalty should be toward the school where they were faculty members and employees of the state. In short, fund raising was an area that never worked well together. Alignment, mentioned in this book repeatedly as very important to both the school and the medical system, was not evident in fund raising, and indeed there were definite competitive feelings on both sides over the years.

The medical system had no endowment in contrast to many if not most other large academic hospitals, including the very prestigious one across town, Johns Hopkins. Most of the medical system fund raising went for immediate capital needs such as the new buildings or special renovations. The Greenebaum gift was the exception; it was directed to the cancer center specifically as an endowment. Most potential donors were not interested in funding a "general" endowment. But an opportunity appeared out of the blue. Jesse C. Coggins, MD, had died in 1963 leaving his estate to Keswick, a retirement/nursing home in north central Baltimore. Coggins, a psychiatrist, operated the Laurel Sanitarium and often referred patients to Keswick for rehabilitation, then known as the Home for Incurables in Baltimore City. One paragraph of the will stated that upon the death of the last of four annuitants under a trust created by the will, the residue of the estate was to go to Keswick Home. The funds were "for the acquisition or construction of a new building to provide additional housing accommodations to be known as the Coggins Building, to house white patients who need physical rehabilitation. If not acceptable to the Keswick Home, then this bequest shall go to the University of Maryland Hospital to be used for physical rehabilitation."

The funds, originally about $3 million, were placed in trust at Mercantile Bank and Trust where the interest was used to support his wife and then his other annuitants until their deaths. At that time the funds were to go to Keswick to build a wing to be named the Coggins Building. Keswick, knowing the money was coming in due time, admitted Mrs. Coggins and went ahead to spend about $11million to construct the new building, giving it the Coggins name. But Coggins had noted in his will that Keswick could only receive the money if it remained for whites only, which it had been in Coggins' segregated lifetime in Baltimore and the south in general. In his will, he noted that if Keswick "could not use" the money, then it should go to the University Hospital for its physical medicine program.

After Coggins' last annuitant died in 1998, Mercantile looked back at the will and noted that University Hospital was mentioned and so notified the medical system. Mercantile, concerned about the "white" clause in the will, filed an interpleader suit to have a court designate how the estate, which had grown over the years to more than $28 million, should be distributed. Was it to go to Keswick or to the Medical System? Keswick had long ago opened its doors to all, consistent with the changing mores of the community and the laws of the times. But did this necessarily preclude it from receiving the Coggins' gift? The case went to court, argued for the medical system by Shale D. Stiller, a noted constitutional lawyer at Piper Marbury. His case rested on the fact that Coggins was a diehard segregationist, and his will made clear his expectations, notwithstanding any changes in the community since. He argued that the clause "if not acceptable to Keswick" meant that Keswick could not take the monies since it was no longer segregated; the estate belonged to the medical system. Various board members held differing opinions as to whether it was appropriate for the medical system to contest the issue. After all, Keswick had built the building and placed the Coggins name on it years before. It anticipated the funds and certainly the medical system never even knew of the will until contacted by Mercantile. And did the medical system want to appear to be arguing for an estate that was dependent upon a segregationist concept? But the decision was to proceed. Meanwhile the case drew national media attention because of the unique issues presented of civil rights versus personal rights in drafting a will. Baltimore City Circuit Court Judge Joseph H.H. Kaplan granted the medical system's motion for summary judgment, and Keswick promptly filed for appeal. The board again discussed the matter and some suggested offering Keswick a portion of the funds if they would not appeal.

The full seven judge Maryland Court of Appeals heard the case and one judge in particular seemed negative toward the medical system's contention. How would they rule? Would $28 million, so close today be gone tomorrow? Rapoport called upon attorney Frank Burch, Piper Marbury managing partner, and encouraged him to look for further possibilities. Burch shortly suggested insuring the decision. He would find a consortium of insurance companies to take the risk that the Court might vote against the medical system. A group of five insurance companies agreed to take the risk for a combined premium of $4 million or $800,000 each, payable immediately as a reserve pending their due diligence. They in turn engaged Charles Ruff of Covington and Burling, the lead lawyer for President Clinton's impeachment defense, to examine the case. During Ruff's career he worked in the United States Department of Justice; during the Watergate scandal, he served as a special prosecutor who investigated President Richard Nixon. He was the United States Attorney for the District of Columbia for some time and represented Anita Hill during Clarence Thomas' Supreme Court confirmation hearings. He believed that the medical system's case was solid; so the insurance companies agreed that they were making "an informed decision" and accepted the policy. There was a sigh of relief, but then came an exceptionally long wait for the court to rule—over two years.

Finally in May, 2002, the appeals court held the estate should go to Keswick. In reaching that decision, the court simply cut the term "white" from Coggins' will. Judge John C. Eldridge, writing for a unanimous court, explained that "this court has long held that where a bequest is conditioned upon the commission of an illegal act or an act which is legally impossible of fulfillment, the condition is invalid on the ground of public policy. Under these circumstances, the condition will not be enforced by awarding the bequest to an alternative beneficiary; instead, the illegal condition will be excised.

Coggins and Burch "Found Money"

The appeals court hearing was contentious, and our legal team was confronted by a hostile judge who appeared to ignore all the precedents that were favorable to our case. Indeed the judge was so obviously biased that the other judges were strangely silent during the entire hearing. At the conclusion of the hearing I was frustrated and quite fearful that we were in danger of losing the appeal. I felt that UMMS was so greatly in need of the capital that this estate was divinely destined for us. How could the court rule against us?

Trying to organize my thoughts and letting my anger subside for 24 hours I called Burch and asked him for help. Not surprisingly my frustration had not cooled in 24 hours.

Burch in his best lawyer/client tone said, "Mort, we just had a hearing, the appeals court has not reversed the lower court opinion. We are going to win this case, but let me get back to you." I was not assured and certainly not mollified. Over the next 72 hours Burch called me almost daily with a series of ideas that might mitigate a potential court reversal. First he suggested we call Keswick and see if they were amenable to a settlement. Since we had won in the lower court and the appeals court had not rendered an opinion, Keswick might be more receptive to settlement. I was mildly interested in that approach; he suggested that I think it over.

Twenty-four hours later Burch called and said "let's roll the dice. Let's negotiate a high-low."

"What's a high-low?" I asked.

He explained that if we win the appeal we get most of the money and share a small amount with Keswick. If Keswick wins the appeal they get more, and we get less. The process of negotiation and settlement will be based on what we and Keswick think are the probable outcomes. Again I was interested in mitigating our risk, but Burch was on a roll and suggested that we think about it a bit more.

A day or two later Burch called and said, "I've got an idea that you might like."

By now I was less angry and very interested in Burch's latest idea.

"My guys in New York think we may be able to insure the decision," he added.

My response was, "What are you talking about?"

Burch said, "Look, AIG and the large reinsurance companies are looking for new product lines to insure. They think that court decisions may be insurable."

Of course the immediate question was, and always is, "What's the premium?"

Within two weeks we negotiated contracts with five insurance companies for a total of $4 million in premiums to insure our potential receipt of $25 million (each company insured $5 million of the estate for an $800,000 premium).

Two years later the Maryland Court of Appeals reversed the lower court and awarded Keswick the Coggins estate. As a result the insurance companies sent us $25 million. In spite of our good fortune with this form of insurance, as I understand it, the major insurance companies in this country have found that insuring court decisions has become a very profitable product line.

-Morton I. Rapoport, MD

LESSONS LEARNED:

Development is essential for an academic medical center. When there was no history of fund raising, no major board commitment, and a strong presence across town at Hopkins, then it seemed that the best approach was to use the leader's ties to the community to develop initial and continuing commitments. It might have been preferable if the medical system and the medical school could have found a way for a single fund-raising organization or at least a coordinated process. But this did not occur and still has not occurred. In its absence the two parties must still work together or risk losing major gifts over time. Success often depends on partnership, and so alignment here would be valuable. Further, both must figure out how to engage the physicians to be functional parts of the fund-raising initiative. And when unlikely sources of new funds appear and then seem on the verge of disappearing, it is useful to step back and consider the issue from a new and creative perspective. Such is what happened after listening to the oral arguments at the court of appeals; rather than accept defeat should the court so rule, the medical system found another approach that ultimately led to a sizable beginning of a general endowment.

CHAPTER ELEVEN

A Time of Transition—An Experiment in Withdrawing Alignment

Conventional wisdom would dictate that at any academic medical center, the medical school dean and the hospital CEO along with their teams and the governance systems should be in alignment. Alignment need not mean working in lockstep together, nor does it mean always agreeing to every request of the other. Indeed, some tension will always exist (frequently described as constructive tension) as each organization seeks to obtain limited resources, but in the end the two must be working for their combined benefit if either is to reach its full potential. Of course the challenge that all institutions face is that they must achieve alignment without great additional cost or loss of institutional identity. This can be difficult at best, and sometimes alignment is not achieved. The results of non alignment can be costly and lead to failure for both institutions.

In medicine we often refer to "an experiment in nature," meaning that we learn about the normal working of the human body by observing and studying a disease. For example, chronic granulomatous disease is a rare pediatric illness with only a few hundred patients diagnosed in the entire United States. These children develop serious infections of a certain type and usually die before reaching adulthood. Over time, doctors and researchers learned that the children's white blood cells did not function properly. The cells engulfed the bacteria as they should, but the bacteria did not die. Researchers discovered that these white blood cells did not manufacture hydrogen peroxide, which proved to be the critical ingredient to kill the bacteria after ingesting by the cell. Later discoveries revealed that the hydrogen peroxide was not produced because these children had a minor yet critical difference in a single gene (out of nearly 20,000 genes) that precluded the production of hydrogen peroxide. So from studying these relatively few children with a serious disease, it was possible to learn how white blood cells in all of us protect against infection. This is the "experiment in nature." After our retirement, a similar experiment was initiated at the medical system, and in the process it revealed just how important alignment was with the school of medicine.

Rapoport retired in September of 2003, 21 years after Farmer had first established the medical system and 19 years after the separate governance legislation. Shortly before Rapoport's retirement, Schimpff retired as chief executive of the medical center; Ashworth, who had been medical center chief operating officer, succeeded him.

Erickson, chairman of the board, led a search committee to select the new system CEO. The committee members were board members of UMMS but specifically included cross-over members of the board of regents, the dean of the school of medicine and the president of the university. Erickson had met and admired Edmund Notebaert, formerly CEO of Children's Hospital of Philadelphia (CHOP), and recommended him to the committee. A search firm brought additional candidates, and eventually it was narrowed down to two finalists. Notebaert got the nod and began in September 2003.

The system had grown to six hospitals and was positioned for further expansion. It had about $1.2 billion in revenue per year, a consistently strong net income, a good bond rating and a relatively strong balance sheet. The medical center recapitalization with new buildings and technology had progressed, allowing for critical physician recruitment and program development. This meant patient referrals and hence admissions had grown significantly. The HSCRC had been generous with rates, resulting in growing cash reserves.

To some of his senior staff and selected board members Notebaert indicated that he was a change agent and would develop a different relationship with the school. The medical system would no longer be so generous with its resources. But he quickly became personally close to Wilson, the dean, and one observer said, "They appear to be riding a tandem bike together."

Alignment appeared to be the order of the day. The system sent substantial monies to the school, especially for faculty salaries. But at some point this close relationship began to fray, even before Wilson retired in the summer of 2006, although the two remained close personally.

Prior to Notebaert's recruitment, Erickson had expressed frustration at what he saw as a lack of seamless care at UMMS. He and Notebaert believed the problem was not the physicians' inability to offer excellent care but rather the physicians' lack of appreciation of how to manage the business side of care delivery. Erickson (and Notebaert) would have preferred to have the practice plan moved under the control of the medical center management. A few academic hospitals have such a structure including CHOP, Notebaert's former institution, where the physician enterprise was a part of the hospital operation. And it was an approach that had been initiated recently at some other academic medical centers around the country. But they knew that at Maryland it would be strongly resisted by the school of medicine leadership.

Notebaert proposed to build an ambulatory care center using UMMS capital that would incorporate all of the medical center's and much of the faculty practice plan's specialty activities (other than primary care) under one roof but with an organizational structure managed by the medical center. Wilson was generally pleased with the plans for the new building but once the organizational structure became clarified, he began to resist. Trust began to erode with the thought that UMMS was attempting to control the physicians' activities and hence their economic lifeline. Was it to be "a new house with free rent" but with "a landlord in control of all activity in the house?" This would not be satisfactory to Wilson. He preferred a "condo" arrangement where the physicians operated their own practices within the new building. Indeed, the building was seen by some in the school as a "Trojan Horse"—once the physicians were in the building, the medical system would be able to exert control and effectively if not actually absorb the practice plan. In that sense, many school leaders saw this as a brilliant strategy by Notebaert and Erickson to gain working if not titular control of the practice plan.

In return, the school offered a "50-50" governance plan for the new building, i.e., a board composed of equal representatives of the school and the medical center. Notebaert rejected that plan. At about this time Wilson retired, and so the definitive agreement—or lack thereof—between the parties was left to be negotiated with the newly appointed dean, E. Albert Reece, MD, PhD, MBA. He proved loath to "give away" control of the practice plan activities—what he perceived as a critical element of his new responsibilities.

An ambulatory care building had been part of the original 1988 master facility plan and was certainly needed for tertiary ambulatory diagnoses and treatments. It had been postponed, largely at the recommendation of the clinical chiefs, until the major inpatient facility construction and renovations had been completed. As of 2004, major inpatient development of new beds still was needed, especially for medical patients, along with resolving the needs of pediatrics and obstetrics (and to a lesser degree psychiatry), which were not addressed in the completed facility upgrades. In the early years of the 21st century, plans had been developed for further construction of beds to address all of these issues. But to Notebaert, ambulatory care seemed essential at the time as outpatients ultimately served as the source of inpatients. His concept was to bring all of the downtown ambulatory care activities (other than primary care) under one roof, both hospital clinics and faculty practice offices. It would also include a new radiation oncology facility, cardiac catheterization laboratories, gastrointestinal endoscopy laboratories, pulmonary function and pulmonary procedure rooms and many more. The faculty practice plan had done its own study a few years before and determined that if they were to move their administrative functions to other locations, the current buildings could handle the need for increased capacity for some years to come. However, they fully agreed that space for what might be termed "tertiary" ambulatory activities was clearly desirable. Notebaert was determined to proceed with the larger building on the belief that it would attract new patients and would soon be at capacity.

The new ambulatory building as planned was an attempt to attract individuals to come to downtown Baltimore from suburban locations for all of their specialty care. Hopkins had tried this approach 15 years earlier with the construction of a major ambulatory care building on the Hopkins Hospital campus and eventually decided it was useful but not sufficient. Hence, Hopkins built its very successful large outpatient facilities to the north (Greenspring Station) and northeast (White Marsh) of Baltimore. Notebaert also proposed to the dean that a new, single, electronic medical record (EMR), paid for by UMMS, should be used in both the medical center and in all of the physicians' offices, including the new ambulatory center. There was general agreement that an effective EMR was critical to the future of medical care. Working together with the help of a physician advisory committee, a vendor was chosen.

Some in the medical school expressed concern that the high cost of the ambulatory building, which they considered too large for the needs per their projections, and the EMR given that one was now in place in the medical center, would siphon off needed dollars from other critical issues, such as program development, new technologies and added inpatient capacity. Although various individuals hold differing opinions today, there were those who believed that the ambulatory building was not an ambulatory strategy but rather a building. Some of those same individuals thought it was a strategy for addressing UMMS preference that it should effectively manage the practice plan activities. In the meantime, there were those within the medical system management who felt that the medical center was losing its strategic advantage because it needed added inpatient capacity, a need not being met. The plan over the past years to bring in other hospitals to the medical system, along with the management of nine other ERs and the operation of Express Care, meant that there was now an increasingly strong referral base for the medical center. Indeed, the center was becoming a "community hospital asset" where the community hospitals could refer their tertiary and quaternary patients for seamless care. But there were no new beds to accept the new patients. Gridlock had ensued, but it went unrecognized or at least unaddressed because of the financial requirements of the ambulatory building and the new EMR system.

The medical system had the capital capacity for the ambulatory building and for the new EMR when they were first proposed in 2004. But when the medical center did not grow its admissions as planned in fiscal 2008, net income fell, and the ambulatory care building and the information system had to be placed on hold. Moreover, by the early spring of 2008, the new dean of the school of medicine did not and would not approve of Notebaert's proposed organizational structure for the ambulatory activities. Meanwhile, the land had been purchased, the old buildings had been cleared, the excavation was nearly complete and the footings were in place. It was decided to go ahead with the underground garage and then wait and determine the next steps as time dictated. Without the ambulatory building going forward and with the shortfall in capital, the new information technology purchase was also put into abeyance.

These were important issues, but concurrently the level of alignment between the medical system and the school/university was rapidly deteriorating. It was clear that the CEO of the medical system and dean of the medical school were not partners, were not in alignment. Their differences were amplified by their senior staffs who were no longer able to reach consensus with each other on many important issues. The governance boards of the two institutions, while aware of the problems, were unable or unwilling to resolve the deepening fissures. The chasm widened with increasing tensions. At least one board member suggested that the CEO resign; others suggested that both the CEO and the board chair resign and still others suggested that the CEO and the dean resign. Eventually, university representatives lobbied the governor to ask for assistance noting that the two parties were unable to function together in an effective manner

Early in the summer of 2008, recognizing that leaders from the university and medical system were no longer in alignment, Governor Martin O'Malley intervened. Within a few months, Notebaert resigned. Later in summer the governor, ignoring proposals of the board chair, placed five new individuals of his own choosing on the UMMS board of directors. He did so believing that the board needed reinvigoration with recognition of the key issues of aligning with the university. This was a distinct change from the past 25 years. Heretofore the medical system board had recommended new members to the governor. In all but one instance, those recommendations had been accepted by the various governors over the years.

A few weeks later 10 board members, led by Erickson, resigned, citing their dismay that the governor had interfered with the workings of a separately established corporation. They believed that the governor had acted inappropriately, albeit within his prerogative, by not allowing the board to recommend their own replacement members. Michael Busch, a member of the board and speaker of the Maryland House of Delegates, was chosen interim chair, and the board then moved to elect Chrencik, the corporation CFO, as interim chief executive officer. Also, in accordance with the UMMS governing statute, at its meeting the next day, the University System Board of Regents elected Chrencik as a vice president

Robert A. Chrencik, UMMS president and CEO

of the university. Chrencik and Reece promptly stated their combined intent to re-establish a strong working relationship and to rebuild the spirit of partnership and alignment that had existed in years' past.

What had happened to create this situation where a governor had felt it necessary to intervene in the function of a board of directors of a corporation meant to be separate from the state government? It is useful to look back as to why the legislature created the medical system nearly 25 years ago.

The vision for privatization was to create a business enterprise to encourage higher quality, effective financial systems and much improved outcomes for patient care. It was also a method for the new medical system leadership to accept the accountability for the new system's success or failure. One of the founding board members frequently stated, "No money, no mission." A truism for sure, but it is critical to appreciate that the mission was the reason for the medical system to exist—"to heal, to teach, to discover." Alignment was a major key to success of the mission and vision. With board encouragement and direction, management tried to practice alignment continuously. University Hospital became an enterprise, but it is critical to recall that it was and is a university hospital. With the legislation, it became the University of Maryland Medical System. Community hospitals were added over time specifically for the purpose of strengthening this university hospital, thus the evolution of UMMS. Although mergers were designed to strengthen the medical center, there was as much if not more positive implications for the community hospitals themselves. Beginning in about 2004 there seemed to be a change in the core philosophy that had been pursued successfully for 20 years—one that is essential for success in an academic medical center. This was the "experiment in nature" alluded to at the beginning of this chapter. In part because of this change in philosophy, a successive series of missteps seriously eroded what had been accomplished. In the end it became clear that when alignment is missing—just as when the gene for hydrogen peroxide is missing—the systems cannot function optimally. Eventually the functions, as happened here, literally implode on themselves. It appears today, a year after the events of the summer of 2008, that alignment and partnership are being addressed in realistic and progressive terms.

Beginning with the creation of the medical system in 1982, the philosophy that guided its management was the constant seeking of alignment with the school and the faculty. Certainly it did not always work right or well, but for about 20 years the constant push-pull for alignment was critical to the successes that occurred. Perhaps it was the authors' physician backgrounds that continuously led them to see the organization as a "patient"—attempting to diagnose and treat it to make it well, make it better and to heal troubled interactions. Whatever the reasons for success in the past, organizational, programmatic and economic alignment with the physicians and the school was and remains essential for each party's success. The independence granted to the medical system by the legislature in 1984 remains critical, but the separate governance of the two organizations must never blind leadership to the critical relationship between the school, the faculty and the medical center/system. It is the authors' hope that this approach will continue to be regained and reinvigorated in the coming years, and thus the medical system can retain its rightful place in the healthcare delivery of the state and region.

LESSONS LEARNED:

The dean and the CEO along with their staffs and the two boards must be in alignment. Alignment need not mean working in lockstep together nor does it mean always agreeing to every request of the other. Indeed, some tension will always exist as each organization seeks to obtain limited resources, but in the end the two must be working for their mutual benefit if either is to reach its full potential.

It is worth noting that alignment is not just an issue for academic health centers. Most community hospitals depend on local physicians to admit their patients. Alignment between the hospital and the physicians is thus absolutely essential—absent alignment and the physicians will seek to admit their patients elsewhere.

An appropriate metaphor is that the organization one is leading is essentially a patient, a patient that needs preventive medicine always and therapy on occasions. A good physician (the governance bodies, the CEO and the dean) will attend to these preventive needs on an ongoing basis and be alert to signs of distress before they manifest as a serious disease.

CHAPTER TWELVE

The Medical System in 2009—25 Years Later and a Peek into the Future

From Failing to Vital in 25 Years

It takes time to change an institution from one management and leadership culture to another and for success to accrue, but it takes many more years for that success to become recognized by the public. After 25 years, the medical system is just now becoming recognized as the regional healthcare powerhouse that it is and for its dedication to "healing, teaching and discovery." As to the future, some definite opportunities lie ahead. The critical factor for the medical system is to recognize that these opportunities will require strategic direction. By maintaining its leadership and using it within the state's levers of power, it can help to assure its success.

The introductory chapter discussed four key themes of the book—alignment with the school and its clinical faculty along with leadership, vision and management; an entrepreneurial orientation; a public-private partnership with the state; and separate governance. These approaches by the medical system leadership, over time, brought a failing hospital to a state of vitality, dynamism and respect with solid financial results, high quality, and world-class programs. The medical system overall grew to be a regional powerhouse, commanding great respect among the business community and state government officials while offering expert care year after year to thousands of patients.

The authors recall a comment years ago by Bray of the national advisory committee when he stated that it takes an institution "at least

20 years not only to become successful but to be recognized as such.
Conversely, once a great institution falls on hard times, it will still be
considered highly as it had been for many, many years."

The medical system exemplifies the first part of this concept. It took
a long time to change the culture to that of a business enterprise with
an entrepreneurial approach, yet one focused on its mission of healing,
teaching and discovery and its vision to be a standard-setting academic
medical center. It took 10 years and the construction of the Gudelsky
Building in 1994 before residents of Baltimore, Maryland and the region,
began to recognize that a new and vibrant institution was present in
downtown Baltimore. But in reality, the medical system, 25 years since
separate governance, is still just gaining recognition as a true regional
health system of distinction and a source of expertise for the city, the
state and the region.

As of June 30, 2009, 27 years after its creation within the university
and 25 years since the separate governance legislation went into effect,
the medical system now consists of nine member hospitals and two affiliate hospitals. It is anchored by the flagship academic acute care hospital—the University of Maryland Medical Center—and has hospitals that
encompass community care in Baltimore, the nearby counties and the region along with specialized facilities for rehabilitation and chronic care.

Maryland General Hospital serves a significant portion of the western side of downtown Baltimore and is a major part of the UMMS
primary care strategy. Kernan Hospital with its new 128-bed Schaefer
Rehabilitation Unit (representing, in part, the former Montebello Rehabilitation Hospital) is the state's largest rehabilitation hospital and a
major provider of orthopedic care. University Specialty Hospital (former
Deaton Hospital) provides chronic care for patients with a variety of
complex illnesses, such as the need for long-term respiratory care. The
Baltimore Washington Medical Center (formerly North Arundel Hospital), a rapidly growing institution, provides comprehensive care to the
northern half of Anne Arundel County and has the state's busiest emergency room. Mt. Washington Pediatric Hospital provides chronic care
services to infants and children, especially those with long-term pulmonary care needs related to prematurity. Easton Memorial Hospital in

Easton and Dorchester Hospital in Cambridge provide comprehensive care to much of the west-central portion of the eastern shore of Maryland, and the recent addition of Chester River Hospital in Chestertown extends the reach of the medical system northward along the eastern shore of the Chesapeake Bay. The two Upper Chesapeake hospitals in Harford County were in close talks with the medical system at the time of this writing.

The medical system represents 12.25% of the acute-care hospital admissions in Maryland, 13.3% of licensed acute-care beds and 14.2% of the total number of patient days in Maryland hospitals. In addition it includes a significant percentage of the rehabilitation beds and many of the chronic-care beds in the state. Its strong financial structure allows for continued development of clinical programs and the required facilities and technologies.

Overall the medical system has grown from about 20,000 admissions to almost 90,000 annual admissions as of June 30, 2009. Revenues have grown from about $100 million annually to over $2.1 billion. Net operating income has grown from about $1.8 million in 1984 to $30 million in 2009 with $185 million in EBIDA or cash flow. [Figure 12-1-4]

FIG 12-1

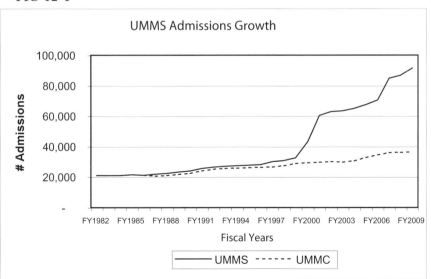

FIG 12-2

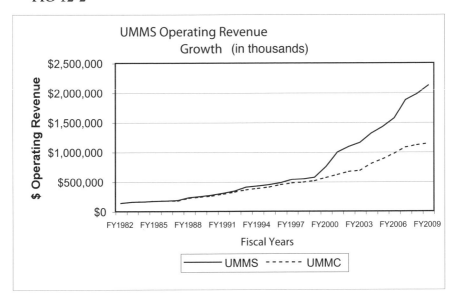

FIG 12-3

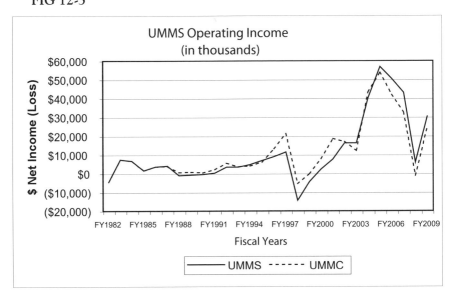

FIG 12-4

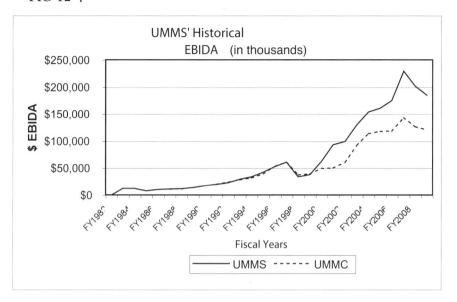

The University of Maryland Medical Center, formerly University Hospital, has witnessed construction of the Shock Trauma building, the Gudelsky and Weinberg patient care towers, and renovation of its 1934 and 1972 hospital buildings, amounting to more than $500 million and almost one million square feet of new construction. Technology is now state of the art, with more than $500 million in imaging, procedure, therapeutic and diagnostic equipment along with greater than $100 million in information technology installations. Concurrently, admissions have nearly doubled from 20,000 to over 36,000; the medical center houses one of the largest kidney transplant programs in the world and is home to Shock Trauma, the premier trauma program in the country. The Greenebaum Cancer Center has recently been certified by the NCI; cardiac care has blossomed, and the high-risk obstetrics and neonatology program is flourishing. Neurocare—including brain attack, multiple sclerosis, and movement disorders—is growing. Radiology and the clinical laboratories are state of the art as is the newly developed "OR of the Future" suite of 20 operating rooms and one of the first full-service surgical simulation laboratories in the country. The emergency room of 1985 with its three full-time physicians has developed into an emergency care network providing physician coverage for 10 of Maryland's hospitals.

The school of medicine has prospered as well. Over 25 years the faculty has grown from 710 to 1,184; total research grants and contracts have grown from $35 million to $377 million while NIH awards have advanced to $249 million; the practice plan income has grown to $194 million, and the school has seen the construction of multiple new research buildings to house its ever-growing research enterprise. It ranks 19th in NIH grants and contracts among all 129 medical schools and ninth among the 76 state-supported medical schools.

In sum, the medical system has become a vital, dynamic system of great importance to the healthcare of the citizens of Maryland and the region. Concurrently the school of medicine has become one of the country's top-ranked schools with an ever-expanding reputation for excellence in teaching and research. The partnership or alignment between these two institutions has been essential for the success of each.

The Hospital of the Future

Given that growth and strength, what can be expected into the future? What will the medical system look like and what will it be doing in the next 10 to 20 years? To address these questions it is useful to consider where American medicine is going as a result of significant gains in the basic understanding of disease and treatment and to consider some demographic, financial and other characteristics that will impact "the hospital of the future."

In the coming years we can expect that medicine will change dramatically such that it will become custom-tailored (also known as "personalized medicine"); there will be greater emphasis on prevention; medicine's ability to repair, restore or replace organs, tissues and cells will markedly advance; medical information will finally become fully digitized with instant access; healthcare quality and safety will improve dramatically; and, in all likelihood, there will be realistic attempts to address the rapidly rising costs of medical care.[6]

These changes are being driven by advances in biomedical research, such as the advent of the genomics era with targeted drugs, drug prescribing with assured efficacy and safety, disease prediction and disease prognostication and improved diagnostics. Also driving change are a developing understanding of stem cells and advancements in our knowledge of immunology, leading to the creation of vaccines for both infections and chronic diseases such as atherosclerosis and Alzheimer's and to methods for improved transplantation including xenotransplantation; and the advances arising from the pharmaceutical and biotechnology industries yielding new drugs.

Less appreciated are the advances in medicine that derive from engineering and computer science. These include vastly improved anatomic imaging and the beginnings of functional or molecular imaging; medical devices, such as pacemakers, stents, bioengineered tissues and nanotechnology devices; improvements in the operating room, such as new instruments, but also the advent of simulation for training, practice and certification, the use of robots for surgery and surgical assistance, and new approaches such as natural orifice surgery. Engineering and computer science are also driving the push to having all medical data digitized, leading to an effective electronic medical record (EMR) with its ability to improve handoffs, assure safety and improve quality. Later on this will lead from information manipulation to knowledge development with data mining, alerts and prompts, and on-demand real time education. Digital medical information will also allow distance medicine to become effective and commonplace, for each person to have and to control his own medical data, and will provide the basis for designing simulation of cognitive function in medical education.

Demand for medical services will expand, hugely driven by a growth in the population, an aging of the population and a shift from acute to chronic diseases as those most prevalent. Consumerism is beginning

NOTES:

6. This section is adapted in part from Schimpff's forthcoming book *The Common Misconceptions of Health Care Reform* and to some degree from his earlier book *The Future of Medicine—Megatrends in HealthCare*.

to have an impact that will spread rapidly and increase exponentially, changing patient expectations as a result. The costs of medical care are high and rising and ultimately will lead to concerted efforts to rein in the rate of rise.

Despite the drivers of change, and the strength of effort behind those drivers, at least as many barriers will prevent, slow down or modify change. Many are financial barriers. Health care financing is fragmented at best and pays for care in a manner that does not encourage primary care, preventive care, care management, disease management or team-based care. Nor does it now pay for eMedicine, such as email, distance medicine or other virtual means of patient care that can, in fact, reduce costs and improve quality of care. Other barriers are professional short-ages and changed professional work expectations. A shortage of nurses and pharmacists exists now, and soon there will be a shortage of physi-cians overall, especially in rural and urban poor areas. A lack of im-portant standards inhibits advances—interoperability is needed for the interaction of devices, such as monitors in the ICU, equipment in the OR and among various electronic medical record products.

Access to capital is severely constricted today because technology and facility costs have escalated dramatically and will continue to do so. The current credit market situation is a further barrier, limiting the hospital's borrowing capacity. This severely limits a smaller hospital's opportunities to grow and develop new programs, to build or renovate and to purchase technology. This will lead to a major wave of hospi-tal consolidations to achieve access to capital markets. Levels of care in the hospital will intensify, and advanced care will consolidate into tertiary centers. Hospital care will increasingly utilize technologies, and hospitalists will do most inpatient care, yet more and more care will be performed at less-intense sites, including home.

Hospital beds will increase in number, intensity and format. More hospital beds will be constructed to serve the added needs of an aging, growing population with complex, chronic diseases. Multiple approach-es will connect specialists and technology. The eICU will become com-monplace with the specialist present physically some of the time and virtually all of the time to both improve care and reduce costs. More rehabilitation hospitals may be constructed, especially as part of hospital systems. More subacute units of general hospitals may be developed, if reimbursement systems so encourage, to give more appropriate care while reducing costs of care. Palliative care and hospice care will become ever more prevalent, and home care after hospitalization will take on a greater role. Unfortunately, the current reimbursement system hampers optimum use of these modalities with their potential to not only improve care but to reduce the costs of care.

Physician shortages will lead to the greater use of nurse practitioners, physician assistants, optometrists, psychologists, and social workers for high-prevalence conditions; as adjunct caregivers in highly complex cases, e.g., cancer; and for chronic care disease management. New forms of professionals will emerge to fill the growing primary care physician gap, such as the doctorate of nurse practitioner. Meanwhile, physician professional expectations will lead to large group practices or hospital employment with less call, more flexible hours, malpractice coverage and little or no management duties. There will be more employed physicians, especially hospitalists and intensivists, and community hospitals will employ more specialists on staff for critical service needs (e.g., neurosurgery, orthopedics). These changes will mean a need for more physician leaders at all levels to assure better interaction and relationships with medical staff.

Given the rise of consumerism and the shift from acute care to complex, chronic disease management, medicine will shift from its current discipline-oriented approach of care to a disease-orientation with care by multi-disciplinary teams. This will drive the development of centers for cancer, cardiac, diabetes care and others and reduce the emphasis on current organizational models of departments of, for example, medicine and surgery or their divisions of cardiology and cardiac surgery or medical oncology and surgical oncology. A related phenomenon will be the development of regional echelons of care especially for acute, emergent conditions, such as trauma, acute myocardial infarction (AMI) and stroke. This will be a major change for the average general hospital, with care being diverted instead to the nearest certified center that, for example, is capable of immediate coronary artery CT scanning, angioplasty and stent placement for AMI.

All medical information will be digitized—once the two key barriers (interoperability and effective physician documentation) are overcome. All data will be in a digital format; the patients will "own" their data and control its access; that data will be easily accessed, transmitted, and secure. The EMR will be designed around physician work flow; so that it will enhance productivity. ePrescriptions and drug order entry with alerts and knowledge built into the algorithms will become the norm. These advances will have a fundamental impact on medical care, quality and safety, costs, and will open opportunities for effective research with data mining.

With the rapidly rising cost of healthcare, technology, when properly deployed (although usually a major driver of increasing costs) will serve as a means to reduce the rising costs of healthcare by reducing workload, improving productivity, accounting for the shortage of professionals, and making hospital care more affordable. This is one of the critical challenges for developers, manufacturers and end users of technologies.

Simulation technology will fundamentally alter the approach to training, practice and certification of procedural-based skills by decreasing training time, increasing competency, measuring decision-making skills and technical expertise. Robotics will offer a major opportunity to improve medical procedures and effectiveness and efficiency of many hospital functions. Not only will there be robotic surgery and a robotic scrub nurse but also robotic distance consults with the patient—e.g., "RoboDoc." Also in the future will be pharmacy robots, supply-chain robots and central sterile-supply robots. Identification devices will allow for the immediate location of a piece of equipment, a pill, a patient or a surgeon at any given time, dramatically improving the supply chain, pharmacy controls, OR effectiveness, and patient safety.

The result of all of these advances will be custom-tailored medicine, a much greater focus on prevention, vastly improved ability to repair, restore or replace organs and tissues, readily accessible and manageable medical information leading to new knowledge and much improved quality and safety.

The University of Maryland Medical System of the Future

Given the current status of the medical system and what we know about future hospital and medical trends, are we able to project what the University of Maryland Medical System of the future will be like? Certainly not with exactitude, but it is possible to suggest the following: medical costs are rising and will continue to do so, and each of the medical system hospitals will need to aggressively address methods to contain these spiraling costs. The costs of new technologies and facilities are also rising rapidly and are frankly beyond the reach of many smaller, stand-alone hospitals. As a result, many hospitals in the coming years will seek partners. The medical system could well be that partner provided it continues to demonstrate alignment with the school of medicine and its ability to share vision and mission with the region. This will prove to be advantageous to all for healthcare delivery, medical education and training, and new approaches to care.

The medical system can be a major leader in healthcare technology advancement. The EMR is a key to the future. The medical system can work both alone and with other systems in Maryland to utilize an effective medical record that is instantly available, secure and complete. Concurrently, the medical system can champion use of various e-technologies, such as email for patient-physician interactions, telemedicine, the use of "RoboDoc," and possibly telesurgery. The medical system can be a leader in the use of simulation to train students and residents in procedural-based specialties and to use simulation to assure and demonstrate competency among its residents and attending physicians. This will be breaking new ground but will put the medical system into a position of true leadership in this country. By partnering with the school of medicine, it can also be a leader in cognitive simulation technologies which will ultimately be of great value in medical education and in lifetime continuing education.

The medical center is and will be a prime location for the introduction of new technologies and approaches to diagnosis and care, whether
that is major equipment, such as newer CT scanners or radiation oncology equipment, the latest in cardiac stents and ventricular assist devices
or the newest drugs and biologicals for treating cancer. We can reasonably predict that the medical center will need more beds, more ICU
beds and more and increasingly sophisticated operating suites. Given
the need for care management and disease management of complex
chronic diseases, it is reasonable to assume that more and more care will
be delivered in a disease rather than a discipline orientation. This will
mean the development of more programs similar in structure and function to Shock Trauma, the cancer center or the Joslin Center for Diabetes. This in turn will mean a need to work closely with the school and
faculty physicians as progress will only come with a change in the current discipline-orientation to one of disease-orientation. This change is
fraught with opportunities for conflict and tension as it will upend long-
standing organizational structures in both institutions but especially in
the medical school.

The medical center as a tertiary care hospital will be the hub of a referral network for many serious acute medical problems (such as trauma
but also including cardiac, stroke and others) and for many complex,
chronic diseases (cancer, neurologic, cardiac, diabetes, others). This will
happen slowly, as state authorities require that patients with diseases
needing prompt treatment from the most experienced staff and the most
up-to-date technologies be sent immediately to centers of excellence,
and as patients with complex chronic diseases insist that they be referred
to specialized centers at least for second opinions if not for actual comprehensive care.

The community hospitals that make up the medical system will have
more patients and older patients and will also need more beds, including
ICU beds. They will begin to develop eICUs and greater use of eMedicine, telemedicine and telesurgery. They will be part of a system or hi-
erarchy of levels of care, especially for serious acute illness such as heart
attacks and strokes. Disease rather than discipline approaches to care

will become more prevalent, and these hospitals will become leaders in care and disease management, thus improving quality and reducing costs of care.

The post-acute-care hospitals in the medical system will be increasingly critical to acute-care hospitals as a venue for extending the care of patients in an effective yet less costly manner. They will see more patients, more complex cases and will require new technologies to assist in rehabilitation and chronic care. Indeed technology will be used by all of the system hospitals to improve productivity, reduce stress of overburdened staff and reduce costs while improving quality and safety.

Safety will become a front-burner agenda item as will quality measures. Indeed the rise of consumerism along with the requirements of regulatory bodies will mean that the board of directors will spend as much time attending to satisfaction, quality and safety as it will to strategic and financial issues.

Given the current and future staff and physician shortages, each hospital will be addressing innovative ways to maximize the workforce and satisfy those same workers so as to retain them for long periods. It will mean careful attention to a positive culture. Culture includes a sense of worth among staff, recognition of the vision and mission and a belief in them, and an understanding of the institution's vision and strategy—all are critical for a strong culture that is patient-centered, focused on safety and quality and yet attuned to the needs of cost management.

Concurrently, hospital physician staffs will need to give constant attention to the needs of their members while helping them convert to disease orientation, a disease and care management focus and encouraging the use of nurse practitioners and other physician extenders in new and creative ways.

The board of directors will need to become ever more involved and will aggressively need to focus not only on strategy and finances but also on costs, quality and safety. A new report defining the attributes of world class healthcare should be required board reading.[*] More and more, they

---

[*] Kizer, KW, et al "Achieving World Class" 2009 Defense Health Board available in the Appendix at *www.health.mil/dhb*

will need to hold the CEO of the medical system and the CEOs of the individual hospitals accountable for each of these parameters. The board members will need to understand the history of the medical system and its development and to appreciate why the school of medicine is so important to the system's ultimate success. They must understand the need for assisting in the research agenda and the importance of educating and training the next generation of healthcare providers. They will need to actively assist the CEO to maintain the spirit of alignment with the school of medicine and its clinical faculty while concurrently insisting via the University of Maryland System Board of Regents members that this must be a two-way arrangement, that the medical school will need to understand and respond to the medical system's legitimate needs in a timely manner and appreciate that not every request from either the school or the clinical faculty can be granted.

In this time of health care reform, concerns about medical care costs (16% of GDP and rising) which are seriously impacting individuals, businesses and government should motivate the medical system into taking the lead in demonstrating approaches to expenditure reductions. Medical costs in America are high for many reasons, but the most important include: the population is aging and, like an old car, parts wear out. Americans have many forms of behavior adversely affecting health—smoking, obesity, poor nutrition, lack of exercise and high stress. Together these are leading to near epidemic proportions of complex, chronic illnesses that persist for life—diseases like diabetes with complications, heart failure and cancer. These chronic diseases account for 70% of all medical expenditures. It is here that concerted efforts are needed. These patients today receive care in an uncoordinated manner that leads to excessive physician visits, laboratory tests, imaging, procedures and hospitalizations. The way to correct for this waste of money and less than quality of care is to develop disease management approaches to coordinate care with either primary care physicians or with specialty physicians acting as orchestrators for all of the involved participants in the patient's care. eMedicine technologies (not currently reimbursed), attention to preventive medicine (not currently reimbursed), and behavior modifications (not currently reimbursed) will assist here. The medical system, in collaboration with the school of medicine, has three excellent, well recognized programs of coordinated care—Shock Trauma, Greenebaum Cancer Center, Joslin Center for Diabetes. These need to be studied and duplicated as appropriate for other complex chronic diseases along with developing approaches to community coordinated care for other illnesses. This will not be easy because—as we have noted throughout this text—disease (patient)-oriented care is not the organizational structure today. Rather, it is discipline (provider)-oriented care that is the norm. This structure is however fraught with high costs, lower quality and lower patient satisfaction. It would be a defining moment for both the medical system and school to lead the nation in developing new approaches to patient care that not only enhance quality but substantially reduce expenditures.

But the medical system will need to be constantly on guard that it does not allow technology advances to outstrip "high touch, high care," indeed loving care—the bedrock of medicine. It will need to remember the importance of culture, attention to caring, that the patient has a disease (rather than the disease exists in the patient), that the patient is part of a family and that the patient is, in the end, the only real customer.

In sum, it can be predicted with some confidence that the medical system will continue to be a major and indeed growing element in the state's and region's healthcare environment. It can be a recognized leader in providing world class care. The likelihood that other hospitals will seek to join the system is high. It can also be predicted that there will be added beds, added ICU beds, more use of technology, greater attention to approaches to deal with critical personnel shortages and attention to culture, safety, and quality. Technology, both information technology and clinical technologies, will be used ever more often to assist in cost management, with algorithms for selecting the correct imaging study and immediate online advice for evidence-based care to both improve quality of care and reduce unneeded or less-effective care. Disease approaches to care will predominate with care management and disease management systems being introduced along with newer technologies for diagnosis, treatment, education and training and competency certification. The medical system, in partnership with the school, will continue to be the site for the education and training of Maryland's physicians and many of the other healthcare providers of tomorrow. We can certainly expect that the medical system, especially the medical center, will be the site for numerous new developments in medical care as a result of high-quality clinical and translational research.

LESSONS LEARNED:

It takes time to change an institution from one culture to another and for success to accrue, but it takes many more years for that success to become recognized by the public. The medical system is just now becoming recognized as the regional healthcare powerhouse that it is and for its dedication to "healing, teaching and discovery." Concurrently, it is difficult to see into the future, but some obvious opportunities lie ahead for the medical system. The critical factor for the medical system is to recognize that these opportunities will require strategic direction; attention to developing medical advances; attention to cost management; appreciation of a new set of expectations by healthcare professionals; recognition of the public's ever changing requirements; the rise of consumerism; appreciation for the critical avenues available to reduce medical costs in a systemic manner; and the absolute requirement for safety and quality. Finally it must always be remembered that care is rendered by individuals, people who do and must care about their patients, and who must have the resources to administer that care. By using its leadership potential within the state's levers of power, the medical system can help to assure its success.

CHAPTER THIRTEEN

Critical Issues for Success
and Lessons Learned

A medical school and its affiliated academic hospital must work together to better each other and to provide a unified "face" to the
community. The combined success of the two institutions is the
only way that each can have true success. Structure is important—
but leadership that constantly addresses alignment is the key.

In 1997 the authors published an article in *Academic Medicine*, the official journal of the AAMC, entitled "Ownership and Governance of University Teaching Hospitals: Let Form Follow Function."[7]

Included was an overview of a 1994 study by the University Health-
System Consortium (UHC), an organization composed of academic
hospitals from throughout the country. UHC, aware of the rapid changes in the marketplace, had carried out an extensive study of academic
health centers (AHCs). One of the consortium's key findings, in an
earlier study report in 1993, was that if AHCs were to preserve their
academic missions, then they had to compete successfully in the current and evolving market. To do so required "the AHC to (1) manage markets (i.e., develop primary care networks, make contracts with
HMOs etc., to assure a continuing supply of patients); (2) manage value
(i.e., reduce costs and increase both clinical and service quality); and
(3) manage change." The earlier study addressed in detail the process

---

NOTES:

7. Schimpff SC and Rapoport MI, "Ownership and Governance of University Teaching Hospitals: Let
    Form Follow Function," *Academic Medicine*, 1997, 72:576-588.

of managing markets and managing value. The latter study focused on the critical consequences of the third requirement, i.e., "the ownership, governance, organization and leadership of the AHC that are needed to effectively manage change."

The key conclusions[8] of that study were paraphrased in the *Academic Medicine* article and are quoted below; please note the frequent reference to "alignment" or words with a similar meaning, the importance of the governance mechanism and the importance of entrepreneurial leadership:

"The market is changing. AHCs as we know them must dramatically reinvent themselves in order to remain financially viable and accomplish their long-standing mission of clinical service, education and research. This implies ownership, governance, organization and leadership that meet the demands of today's marketplace, including the abilities to act with speed and decisiveness, to manage risk, to develop primary care capacity, to provide a unified response, to collaborate with providers and insurers, and to demonstrate value (i.e., cost and quality).

1. No single structure guarantees an AHC's success, but all AHCs should have an organization with common elements, including an integrated delivery system with a clear strategic plan, a common vision, a unified structure, and a change-oriented and risk-taking culture with a governance that is supportive and accessible.
2. Leadership is the critical variable in managing change. The leader(s) must assume a change-oriented style that encompasses substantial risk-taking. To do so, the leader requires the support of governance.
3. AHCs must capitalize on what should be a competitive advantage by linking physician and hospital components into an integrated clinical enterprise.
4. The faculty practice organization must be reconfigured into an in-

NOTES:

8. University HealthSystem Consortium. Responding to a Dynamic Health Care Marketplace: Implementation Strategies for AHCs. UHC 1995 Research Conference, January 5-6, 1995, Coronado, California (unpublished meeting materials).

tegrated, multi-specialty group practice. This will require profound changes in the culture, structure and behavior of the faculty.

5. Effective governance is essential for the AHC to fulfill its mission while successfully competing in the marketplace.

6. The ownership structure must allow the AHC to act with speed and flexibility. "These conditions will be difficult for most AHCs to meet but first and foremost is the need for a structure of governance that allows the other six conclusions to be addressed. Most institutions that have undergone governance changes report that some action-driving event, often financially based, as at the University of Maryland or the University of Colorado, was the catalyst needed to create the momentum for change. Similarly, the need to address the managed care market environment has driven the University of Minnesota, the University of Michigan and Stanford University to pursue organizational structure changes recently announced or planned."[9]

The study from UHC was clear in the need for an appropriate governance that allows for speed and flexibility but also the need for a change-oriented leadership style; the need for a vision of the future and a clear strategic plan to get there; the need for the hospital and the faculty physicians to work together as partners; the need for the physicians' practice plan to be integrated and flexible with clear leadership; and for the combined hospital-medical school-practice plan to act as a concerted enterprise. All of this implies alignment among the hospital, the medical school and the faculty with its practice plan. As the UHC study suggested, there are many routes to achieving an effective organizational structure and governance; the key is to have one that works and to have the needed alignment to be effective, along with the appropriate leadership and leadership approaches, including an engaged governance.

NOTES:

9. The study was done in consultation with Lewin-VHI and utilized task forces and senior leaders from over 20 institutions representing schools of medicine, the parent universities, academic hospitals, the Association of American Medical Colleges, and the Association of Academic Health Centers. The study was done throughout calendar years 1994 and presented to the membership in January 1995. At the time, Rapoport was on the UHC Board of Directors and Schimpff was a member of the study group.

Let's Not Rock the Boat

I was invited to be a member of the UHC task force. It was made up of individuals from various roles in academic medical centers such as medical school deans and hospital CEOs. The first task was to settle on an agenda for work scope and then to choose a consultant to collect and analyze the data for the task force. Immediately it became apparent that many in the group, led by the deans, were anxious about the eventual recommendations. They were determined that no report would suggest any diminishment for their role and authority within the medical center governance. I was not surprised at this maneuvering, but it meant from the beginning that there were definite forces that would work to limit the nature of the final recommendation. In the end the recommendations never threatened any entrenched interests, nor did they need to in order to offer constructive advice. But it took longer and was more work to get to the end than should have been necessary.

-Stephen C. Schimpff, MD

In the 1994 article in *Academic Medicine*, the authors reviewed the first 12 years of our medical system; how it came to be and what they saw as the most important reasons for success as of that time and what they believed was needed going forward. The following material comes from that article, either quoted directly or paraphrased.

"Change comes with difficulty in any setting, but is particularly difficult to achieve in the academic community because of its customary consensus-based approach to decision-making. Over the past decade, however, the ability to rapidly adapt has been critical to the success, if not the survival of hospitals, and it is increasingly critical to the survival of the entire academic clinical enterprise. The external environment is more demanding than ever, with the pressures of cost containment, technology advancement, competition for market share and serious manpower issues. In addition to the resource issues, changes in medical practice patterns and technology are shifting services to the ambulatory care setting while reducing lengths of stay; patients, families, and payers are demanding accountability from providers for quality and service;

payers are demanding financial concessions; and, perhaps most important, there has been a dramatic shift in the responsibility for financial risk towards the provider.

"In 1980 the University of Maryland Hospital was a provider-oriented rather than a patient-oriented institution, and could be described as having a vision of 'patient care in a teaching setting.' In effect, the hospital's principal mission was that of the University—education and training, with the provision of patient care a required venue in the educational process. Further, state ownership created serious operational impediments to effective management in an increasingly competitive healthcare delivery marketplace. The impediments included rigid state personnel and procurement systems, lack of advocacy at the highest levels of government, and inability to enter the debt market to meet mounting capital needs."

When this article was published the University of Maryland Medical System had been in its new governance status for 12 years and had "witnessed the rapid development and progress of the new corporation as measured by consistent and improving economic viability, a major facility-renewal program, culture change towards patient-centered operations, and more competitive recruitment of faculty and residents. These changes, however, have not been achieved without tension." The authors then noted a critical element in the institution's success. "Progress has required the development of a partnership between the school of medicine and the medical system; so that the new vision of a 'standard-setting academic hospital of distinction' could become a reality.

"The hospital had operated like any state agency in Maryland, in that it received both an operating budget and a capital budget each year. Revenues from patient care were returned to the state treasury; the incentive for financial operational improvement was therefore very limited. There were numerous bureaucratic hurdles related not only to finances but also to personnel and purchasing. Salary guidelines, for example, were set by the state; so that rapid changes in compensation for nurses or other health professionals were not possible. The absence of strong advocacy for the hospital in the upper levels of government meant limited capital funds were made available except in response to regulatory requirements. Further, control of capital for renovation or construction, once approved, was by another state agency; so there was no incentive for hospital management to control costs, timetables or quality on site. Once a project was undertaken, planning was also done through yet another state agency, causing the time to complete a project to be significantly longer than that required in similar private-sector initiatives. In short, given the structural impediment coupled with the rapidly changing health care environment, it appeared likely that University Hospital would continue on a path toward increasing mediocrity."

Many in Maryland during the early 1980s believed that a group of critical goals needed to be achieved: "the clarification of mission and vision, dedicated advocacy by a board chosen for its business savvy and healthcare delivery, an ability to better compete in a rapidly changing healthcare environment (hence dedicated and private personnel and purchasing systems, freedom to contract, freedom to enter joint ventures, etc.), the ability to enter the capital markets, and the authority to manage facilities and equipment upgrades, all while maintaining and indeed strengthening academic pursuits in partnership with the University."

Farmer, the chancellor, "believed that a critical element in the success of the overall medical complex was through dedicated advocacy and improved management of the hospital. Indeed, he maintained that success of the medical school ultimately could not be achieved without dramatic change in the hospital governance structure. He thought it was critical that the hospital be patient-oriented, and this meant a change in culture to one where patient care was the driving force while the absolute requirement for education and research was maintained. His strategic concept in concert with the (university) board of regents was to create an ownership and governance mechanism distinct from the state and University."

Mission for any hospital and certainly for an academic hospital is very important. "In Colorado, the change in the governance occurred with the recognition that the two-fold, well-defined mission of education and indigent care was threatened due to financial losses. Legislation creating the governing authority was perceived as a change in form, not in substance. The CEO of the University of Colorado Hospital at that time (Dennis Brimhall) believed that the clear delineation of a mission prior to legislation was key to acceptance and hence early success. There has been positive dramatic change in Colorado with improved net worth and cash, size, scope and perceived quality of programs and improved physical plant. However, these changes alone were seen to be insufficient to maintain viability given the low hospital occupancy in Denver. Thus, absent the medical school and its need for a teaching hospital, University Hospital would close as a result of market forces. Thus, for Colorado, the educational mission is critical to existence irrespective of the excellence of patient care."

The situation at Maryland was somewhat different. "The mission of the medical system was not made explicit in the enabling legislation other than by inference with inclusion of University representatives on the board (three members of the board of regents plus the dean, the president and the chancellor), the requirement of the medical staff to have university faculty appointments, and the responsibility for care for the west Baltimore community population."

Although the mission was not specifically defined in the legislation, it was implicit that the medical system mission would include patient care, education and research as at any academic medical center. The question was how to support education and research while giving patient care primacy. "From the beginning, however, the medical system's leaders had a basic vision for the future to change the culture from one of provider-orientation to one of patient-orientation. The cultural change, with all that it implied, was to result in an institution with improved facilities and equipment, to provide incentives for patient referrals and thereby allow recruitment of the best and the brightest faculty, staff and students. The aim was to create a standard-setting academic hospital of distinction, a fitting partner for the medical school." Thus, despite the reservations of some that a separate hospital corporation would not serve the interests of the medical school, the leadership considered part-

nership or alignment essential for both parties. But alignment is not easy
to achieve and without question there were, continue to be and will be
in the future tensions among the various parties. The key is to recognize
the tensions and respond in effective and appropriate ways.

"Earlier, we noted that the legislation created some impediments
to success, yet progress has been achieved, although the road to it was
tortuous and fraught with tensions and occasional conflicts. Critical to
success is a board that insisted upon, and leadership that subscribed to
(1) a focus on a limited number of key objectives, (2) an attention to
fundamentals, and (3) a readiness to act and respond to change. Perhaps
most important was (4) a clear vision even when the exact steps to reach
that goal were not always obvious. The strategic plan that the board
adopted was developed by using an integrated, thought out, consensus-
seeking process based upon data. It was action-oriented, with timelines
and accountabilities."

University Hospital in 1984 was financially grossly underperforming,
had deficient facilities and woefully outdated technologies. As a result,
"the first key steps were to achieve financial stability, and to move ahead
to supply the institution's immediate physical needs, followed by a long
range master plan for facilities, driven by the strategic plan, and a ratio-
nal assessment of external sources of funds and internal opportunities to
enhance productivity."

Alignment did not come automatically nor easily. It took years to
engage, to foster and to enhance. Indeed, alignment was not effective
initially and that led to much tension. After the 1987 attempt to oust
Rapoport which in turn highlighted the need for strong alignment, "a
number of steps were taken to improve the partnership between the
university and the medical system. The board of directors amended its
by-laws to make the chancellor the vice-chairman of the board, and to
make either him or the dean the chairman of the strategic planning
steering committee. Several clinical chiefs and senior faculty were assigned to each board committee. Annual board-chiefs-management re-
treats were held. Monthly clinical chiefs management sessions focused
upon financial, operational, planning, and facilities issues to assure that

the clinical leadership was fully informed and had adequate opportunity for input before decisions were made."

By the time the article was written 12 years after the creation of the medical system, the alignment was working reasonably well. Time and trust were important elements of achieving alignment along with improvement in the physical plant, the purchase of much-needed technology and the recruitment of new faculty leaders who had built impressive clinical programs. "Time to adjust to the major changes that have occurred was also important. Time has brought acceptance, by the university leadership and the faculty, of the board and the management team for their dedication and effectiveness and, conversely, the board and management team have learned to recognize the value systems and vision of the dean, the clinical chiefs and their faculty. The best description of what has transpired over recent years is that there has been an evolution of an effective partnership that has engendered mutual respect and collaboration. Learning to work together yet with separate governance systems and complimentary but not identical missions and goals, has been a challenge but also a source of satisfaction, since the overall outcome thus far has been both significant and positive."

The authors believed then and now that the board of directors has been critical to success—success of the medical system directly but also to the joint alignment with the school, the university, the faculty physicians, and the state government and its agencies, such as the rate-setting commission. "The board of directors was...the connection between the vision (to serve the public first rather than internal constituencies) and governance. Serving the internal provider (faculty, nurses, and other professionals) is typical of university-owned academic hospitals, and serving the employee first is typical of a state entity (job-producing or job-sustaining versus serving the public). Both cultures had to be changed; a new board represented the change from state to private ownership and the change from university to private governance. The board functioned because it stayed focused and kept its vision ever in sight. It was proximate to the action, was clearly identified with the enterprise, and was insistent that the hospital must succeed in the competitive marketplace.

As already stated, the board was able to succeed largely because it was separate from the state and the university."

The authors' observations in 1997 mirrored that of the UHC study from 1994. "A critical finding of the University HealthSystem Consortium study is the importance of a readily accessible board that is committed and informed and that will rapidly approve, modify or reject proposals. The consortium's (1994) study noted that at the six institutions that changed governance as of 1994, (i.e., Maryland, Arizona, Florida, West Virginia, Colorado and Chicago) no one interviewed today would recommend returning to the prior structure."

These were the authors' observations when the medical system was about 12 years old. Now at the 25-year mark, the lessons learned are essentially the same, but with time they have been modified as the authors have witnessed the growth, development and maturity of the medical system. In the 1997 article, great emphasis was given to the board of directors as the single critical ingredient for success. While we still believe the board has been essential and critical, we now believe that the board has been effective as long as it and the leadership of both the medical system and the university maintained alignment. Restated, alignment is critical to effectiveness, and the board is critical to assuring that alignment occurs and is maintained.

The metaphor used in the Foreword is worth repeating here. Just as a person needs to have his vertebrae of the spine well aligned one atop the other; so too must the medical system be in close alignment with the faculty physicians, the school of medicine, the state government, the rate setting commission and others. Without this alignment, just as the person will stoop, develop various illnesses and have an early death; so the medical system must slowly but surely lose its credibility with the state government, the enthusiastic and good will and hard work of the faculty physicians, the platform for arguing its case to the rate commission and its opportunity to benefit from the research and education activities of the school of medicine. (The same can be said for most any academic hospital that is part of an academic medical center and although the issues are somewhat different, the principle is the same for a community hospital aligning with, at least, its community physicians.)

Today the medical system and the university are once again addressing the best possible organizational relationships among the key
entities—hospital, medical school and practice plan. Should there be
structural changes or alterations in the reporting relationships? Differences in the flow of funds? And do the entities have congruent missions
and visions and the goals needed for achieving those missions? This has
been a time for reflection and for consideration of what others across the
country are doing or have done while facing the same challenges. For-
tunately, the medical system can look to a wealth of recent publications
and studies for guidance; here is a summary.

AMCs go through periods, depending on current external circumstances, of having a particular interest in one approach or another to
ensure their economic success or even survival. For example, in the late
1970s and early 1980s a number of state-owned and some university-
owned hospitals were divested from state ownership or from their parent
university/ medical school or both, usually to overcome deteriorating
financial situations and the burdens that state personnel and purchasing
systems imposed on the hospital. In the 1990s many AMCs, concerned
about the rise of managed care, looked for ways to "own covered lives."
And, as they then saw the possible coming loss of referrals, AMCs ex-
plored purchasing the practices of primary care physicians in the communities that historically referred tertiary patients to the faculty specialists practicing in the teaching hospital. In the 2000s, AMCs are once
again looking at the organizational framework of their institutions out
of concern for improving financial performance.

Many organizational models exist, but they can be seen as forming a
continuum from largely decentralized to highly centralized under a single governance system (Figure)[10]. Examples of the former would include
the Dartmouth Medical School—Mary Hitchcock Hospital—physicians
practice plan. At the centralized end of the spectrum would be the Mayo
Clinic which includes its physician practice plan (the original "Mayo

NOTES:

10. Modified from Levine, JK, "Considering Alternative Organizational Structures for Academic Medical
     Centers," www.ecgmc.com, 785/60/44644 (doc-E).

Clinic"), the Mayo hospital and the more recently created Mayo Medical School, all under one organizational roof. Toward the center of the spectrum would be Columbia—Presbyterian Hospital or Cornell—New York Hospital where the medical school and the practice plan are part of the university organization, and the hospitals (now merged) are separate. The University of Maryland structure is similar, with the school and practice plan under the umbrella of the university and the hospital (University of Maryland Medical Center) part of the now nine-hospital University of Maryland Medical System.

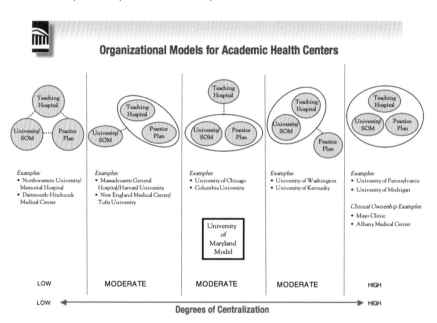

Organizational Models for Academic Health Centers

Examples:
- Northwestern University/ Memorial Hospital
- Dartmouth-Hitchcock Medical Center

Examples:
- Massachusetts General Hospital/Harvard University
- New England Medical Center/ Tufts University

Examples:
- University of Chicago
- Columbia University

University of Maryland Model

Examples:
- University of Washington
- University of Kentucky

Examples:
- University of Pennsylvania
- University of Michigan

Clinical Ownership Examples:
- Mayo Clinic
- Albany Medical Center

LOW   MODERATE   MODERATE   MODERATE   HIGH

LOW ◄──► HIGH
Degrees of Centralization

In 2001, Jay Levine[11] of the consulting firm ECG presented his concepts to the council of teaching hospitals at the AAMC annual meeting. He noted that many think "a different model would solve our problems" but that no "single preferred organizational structure for an AMC" exists. Rather it is important to determine what is best for an individual

---

NOTES:

11. Levine, JK, "Considering Alternative Organizational Structures for Academic Medical Centers," www.ecgmc.com, 785/60/44644 (doc-E).

setting based on a combination of history, politics, economics and many other factors. He advised that rather than searching for an ideal that may not exist, it would be better for AMC organizations to focus instead on "strengthening the hospital-medical school-practice plan relationships," and to do so by addressing the "value that accrues from the various operational and financial attributes" of the current structure. In short, the "management systems and the operating systems must be efficient, coordinated, and not duplicated; financial arrangements must be based upon sound business principles and linked to performance standards." Among the areas he suggested for attention were codifying the hospital's support of faculty salaries; coordinating the financial objectives of the AMC with those of the faculty; and vesting the chairs/service chiefs in the hospital's performance—all steps to creating alignment.

But concern among many AMCs persists that they need to look carefully at their structures in order to ascertain what would be best in today's environment. As a result, in 2004, the University HealthSystem Consortium completed a major study entitled "Supporting the Academic Mission in Difficult Times." The study concluded that "resource constraints are putting pressure on all aspects of the AMC, with all indications that this pressure will increase. As our resource needs exceed our ability to generate them, unavoidable trade-offs will require transparent and effective governance, mutually supportive partnerships, and long-term financial planning. The traditional partners in an AMC (the hospital, the medical school and the faculty practice plan) need to work together as never before to maintain excellence in the three missions of education, research and patient care."[12] The UHC work group (table below) identified three critical performance domains: oversight (governance and the role of governing boards), partnership (the executive leadership of the respective partners and their interrelationships); and financial planning (making difficult decisions regarding the allocation of investment of limited resources to optimize the whole). UHC noted

---

NOTES:

12.   University HealthSystem Consortium, 2004, "Supporting the Academic Mission in Difficult Times."

that these were guiding principles, not prescriptive behaviors, because principles will always apply even when circumstances, organizational dynamics and cultures will vary across AMCs. Thus "effective leaders supported by engaged governing boards, will know how best to embrace the guiding principles and implement constructive change within their own environments." A chart from the study is self explanatory and clearly emphasizes the need for alignment especially in the realms of partnership and financial planning:

PERFORMANCE DOMAINS

	Oversight	Partnership	Financial Planning
Guiding Principles	Engaged Governance	Balance of Missions	Optimization for the Whole
Culture	Accountability	Trust	Discipline
Ideal Practice	Vertical Transparency Fiduciary Leadership Strategic Vision	Horizontal Transparency Sustainable Exchanges Mutual Respect	Coordinated Capital Planning Open Communication Strategic Allocation
Threats	Conflict of Interest	Mission Imbalance	Silo Spending

Despite these and other admonitions to focus on partnership/alignment and not on structure, there continues to be great interest in the organizational structure of AMCs. In September 2008, *Academic Medicine* included a series of articles on structure but also on the various ways AMCs can address alignment. Each article was written by a leader from a major AMC and had its own perspective based largely on the circumstances of the situation at the author's AMC. The observations and suggestions varied from article to article, but they can be summarized by stating that the best structure will vary depending on the particular circumstances of the individual AMC. But more importantly are the efforts of the managerial leadership and the governing board(s) to assure that the parties are effectively working together with a shared vision and agenda. Only with this very human element of alignment, regardless of the nature of the structural alignment, will the institutions be effective in the pursuit of their missions.

The issue of *Academic Medicine* began with an overview by Dr. Steven Wartman, president and CEO of the Association of Academic Health Centers (AAHC); excerpts of his perspective are included here.[13] "... I have seen firsthand the management and leadership challenges that are changing fundamentally the ways in which these organizations operate. These challenges have catalyzed a remolding of the academic health center (AHC) from an ivory tower to a complex business enterprise that captures the power of a virtuous cycle, whereby clinical revenue and academic performance support each other by being strategically and tactically aligned. The virtue is that each makes the other better.

"Apparent in all of the articles is the critical need to achieve strategic alignment, a form of the virtuous cycle, amongst the various components of the institution in order to be successful. Viewed collectively, they address an underlying and unifying theme: the importance of striving for strategic alignment of the enterprise as a whole."

The following quotes (five of the 10 he used are reprinted here) from these articles, taken as a group, present a well-articulated perspective on the issues surrounding institutional leadership, governance, management, and finance for the evolving AHC enterprise.

"Unless we are more creative and tenacious in transcending university and hospital organizational structures, we run the risk of jeopardizing our collective future..."[14]

NOTES:

13 Wartman, SA, "Toward a Virtuous Cycle: The Changing Face of Academic Health Centers," *Academic Medicine*, 2008, 83:797-799.
14. Sorensen AA, "The Transformation of Research in the Health Professions at the University of South Carolina," *Academic Medicine*, 2008, 83:832-836.

"In an academic health center (AHC), research and clinical success are synergistic and interdependent..."[15]

"... the relationships between leaders are often the most important factor determining success or failure..."[16]

"The fundamental challenge of leadership development was to get leaders to think, feel, and act as members of the same team..."[17]

"... the academic missions of the AHC can be substantially advanced with the financial support that the clinical enterprise has traditionally been able to provide..."[18]

Wartman continues, "It is clear that the central challenge for AHCs is to develop a form of the virtuous cycle in which clinical revenue and academic performance are functionally and strategically supportive of each other. Absent major changes in health care financing, this is critical for the growth and success of the AHC enterprise. If research is their ultimate scholarship and education their raison d'être, then patient care is the coin of the realm.

"Not surprisingly, these trends and challenges have led to changes in leadership—the types and kinds of leaders being sought—and in the methodologies of academic administration. There is much more specificity now in leadership searches, and executive search firms, when they are used, are increasingly looking to find candidates with specific skill sets as opposed to general academic credentials. Especially valued are people with communication skills, including vision setting, team building and fund-raising, willingness to share the spotlight with others, a collabora-

---

NOTES:

15. Levine AS, Detre TP, McDonald MC, et al. "The Relationship Between the University of Pittsburgh School of Medicine and the University of Pittsburgh Medical Center—A Profile in Synergy," *Academic Medicine*, 2008, 83:816-826.

16. Pizzo PA, "Case Study: The Stanford University School of Medicine and its Teaching Hospitals," *Academic Medicine*, 2008, 83:867-872.

17. Sanfilippo F, Bendapudi N, Rucci A, Schlesinger L, "Strong Leadership and Teamwork Drive Culture and Performance Change: Ohio State University Medical Center 2000-2006," *Academic Medicine*, 2008, 83:845-854.

18. Barrett DJ, "The Evolving Organizational Structure of Academic Health Centers: The Case for the University of Florida," *Academic Medicine*, 2008, 83:804-808.

tive mindset, and administrative capabilities that facilitate the effective execution of plans and goals."

With this background from the authors' observations 10 years ago and from those of many others addressing the same or similar issues, here, then, is a summary of the four themes of this book—which are also the four key factors that brought success to the University of Maryland Medical System and will maintain its success into the future.

Theme One—Alignment is Critical

This book's first theme is that alignment with the school of medicine and with its clinical faculty was and is critical for the success of all parties. Alignment was also needed with the state government, the rate-setting commission and many others. Alignment with the physicians was an absolutely essential requirement for success. Physicians needed to be listened to, engaged in the process of renewal and made to feel—rightfully so—that they were a part of the solution. It is important to remember that, unlike any other business setting, it is the physicians who bring the patients to the hospital, not the hospital itself. Indeed, a hospital without physicians is an empty hospital.

Similarly, alignment with the school of medicine has been equally critical. The success of the medical system was contingent upon a close alignment with the leadership of the school of medicine and with that of the university. Close personal relationships are valuable as well, but it is the structural alignment of vision, mission, strategies and priorities that is the key to success. Everyone needed to understand that only "win-win" outcomes were adequate. A "win-lose" outcome ultimately would mean a "lose-lose" situation for both the school and the medical system. Alignment required leadership on both sides, of course, and the long period of leadership turnover within the university presidency (from Farmer's death until Ramsey's appointment) was an impediment to effective alignment.

Our observations of what transpired from 2004 to 2008 suggest to us that alignment was not fostered. The medical system leadership and the school and university leadership must be in alignment. For sure, the medical system leadership, both its CEO and its board chair, believed in good conscience that a new approach was the appropriate way to go into the future, but the school and university leadership did not agree. The issues were never resolved, and the differences escalated to overt controversy between medical system and university/school leadership and then reached the level of the board of directors of UMMS and the board of regents of the university system. When the two boards could not agree, the governor finally intervened. This emphasizes why alignment is so critical. Absent alignment, it is not possible for either the school of medicine to reach its full potential or for the medical system to be successful. Their fates are intertwined, not separate. Neither can "go it alone" and expect to be successful.

Separate governance was essential, but if the resulting entity was a "negative asset," as frequently stated by Lipitz, the second board chair, then no amount of effective management could overcome the deficiencies. It was therefore necessary for the state to recapitalize or at least join in a public-private partnership to assist in the recapitalization. But once the recapitalization was started and well along, the system was able to continue the process.

The public-private partnership did not just happen because the state government looked favorably on the medical system. The essential first step was to develop credibility, and that meant achieving a respectable financial status, which in turned allowed the development of credibility in the business and banking community. Meanwhile, developing credibility with key state agencies, especially the HSCRC was critical. Treating state government officials as partners and friends rather than as adversaries was a valuable step in developing credibility. Finally, it became possible to approach the governor and the legislature for assistance with the needed capital upgrades. In essence, the medical system had by then aligned with the state government by accepting accountability for its own financial status and management and providing a track record of some years to demonstrate viability and persistence. In retrospect, UMMS needed to first align with the state. Indeed, this strong and developing alignment with the state government proved to be the medical system's greatest strength, a strength that provided it "clout" with many organizations, institutions and potential partners including the rate commission, the banking community, potential donors and, of course, the university, its medical school and the faculty physicians. This increase in leverage allowed the medical system to advance its strategies with its partners. One might look upon this as a vertical alignment—like the spine—with the first step being alignment with the state government and then alignment with each of the other critical partners over time.

Theme Two—Entrepreneurial Management

Our second theme is that of entrepreneurial management. We believe that an entrepreneurial approach was very effective in changing the culture of the medical system, especially in the early years after privatization. A change of culture into one which was entrepreneurial and business oriented while retaining and remembering the purpose for existence was another essential element. The authors believe that a reasonable degree of intelligence and a lot of patience were likewise important to success as well. In their roles, the authors were "impatient" but still recognized that they needed to "be patient," realizing how long it would take to be truly successful as an institution.

Success required a strong management team, one that was collaborative with each other and with the physicians in the school. It is the authors' contention that an established management team is highly advantageous. Certainly there is value and even a necessity to introduce new members to the management team, just as it is likely that successful managers will occasionally depart for other institutions when offered opportunity for advancement. But an experienced team with institutional history means a certain consistency in management style and approach; the physicians and staff come to know what is expected, and the management team in turn knows the physicians' agendas. Rapid turnover in management inevitably slows action and decision-making and means that a strong institutional culture cannot be created and nurtured. Surprises in an organization are rarely beneficial.

Entrepreneurship, highly useful in developing clinical programs, proved particularly effective with a program that was otherwise not ready for investment. The medical system had a minimal presence in kidney transplantation in 1987, and it was felt that the combination of expense to build a transplant program and competition from Johns Hopkins and other institutions would be too much to overcome. However the opportunity to recruit an entrepreneurial young transplant surgeon proved inescapable, especially since the transplant surgeon's requests were reasonable. He asked simply for a chance to start the program and a promise that as he built it the institution would continue to add support. It proved to be an effective partnership and within 10 years the medical center was doing more kidney transplants than any other institution in the country or the world. Such was the power of recruiting the right individual with the entrepreneurial interest and skills (albeit not yet tested at that time) along with a commitment of support over time provided the program made progress. This approach was successful with many other programs over the years as well.

Theme Three—Leadership, Vision, Strategy, Prioritization with Oversight by an Engaged Board of Directors

Our third theme is that renewal required leadership, vision, and then a comprehensive and agreed-to strategy along with prioritization especially of clinical program development; all were essential for success.
Likewise, a committed board of directors that understood the nature of governance but did not overly interfere with management was a major advantage.

With a clear vision, an organized strategy, and alignment with the physicians and school, it was then essential to select the correct programs for investment. The data-based decisions stemming from the strategic planning activities starting in 1987–88 that led to focusing on trauma, cardiac care, cancer care, neuro-care, high-risk obstetrics and neonatology, and rehabilitation proved to be well founded.

Cancer was an obvious area for investment, but the prolonged struggle over discipline versus disease orientation held back program growth despite investments. This just emphasizes the need for clear resolution of structural and organizational issues—resolutions of a type that cannot occur without alignment with the school of medicine leadership. But even with alignment and the best of intentions by all parties, the disease versus discipline issue is a basic stumbling block in many if not most academic medical centers. It is our contention that a disease orientation in a hospital makes sense and is the way of the future. This is particularly important given that medicine is changing dramatically, with more and more diseases being chronic and complex. These generally lifelong chronic diseases, such as diabetes, heart failure and others, mean that a patient needs a team approach to care, not a single physician, not a single discipline such as medicine or surgery. The same can be said for many acute problems, such as trauma, and those such as cancer that often require many years of treatment and many disciplines to work together for the patient's benefit. Indeed well coordinated care is the key to reducing the high and rising costs of medical care in America overall; a challenge that the medical system and medical school may well wish to pursue into the future.

It has been noted previously that although the strategic planning process strongly suggested investing in orthopedics, it was impossible to do so as long as the divisions between the school and Shock Trauma and the department of surgery and Shock Trauma were still ongoing. It was necessary to put orthopedics aside until the resolution of those issues occurred more than 10 years later.

Along with selecting the correct programs for investment was the need for careful allocation of scarce resources including money, space, renovations and technology. Once the strategic plan was completed, a capital needs assessment and then a technology acquisition plan were developed, the latter in consultation with ECRI, a non-biased, not-for-profit technology assessment organization. While no plan is perfect, the faculty physicians came to appreciate that with prioritization and then reinvestment of success, each program would ultimately be addressed, albeit some more in-depth than others.

The board of directors greatly aided management. From its inception, the deeply engaged board understood the difference between governance and management. It expected to govern, and it expected the

CEO and his team to manage. The board gave good advice and stabilized and strengthened management when necessary. Each board chair gave an enormous amount of time to working with the CEO. Individual board members tutored individual management members based on their own experience in business and management.

The board overall, but especially its leadership, made clear the parameters of separate governance when the system was threatened with disruption by well-meaning clinical leaders who unfortunately did not appreciate how to manage into the future. The board recognized that they themselves were indeed the governance, and that they could not allow the clinical leadership to assume that role. Yet they recognized that it was critically important to listen closely to the clinicians and understand their agenda.

It is the authors' contention that the board was as effective as it was for at least two reasons. The first was that it was made up of exceptionally high-quality individuals who had proven themselves in the business, civic or philanthropic communities. Each had been on multiple boards in the past and was no stranger to the concept of governance even if they did not necessarily know very much about the specifics of health care. But some did, and all were comfortable in asking questions. None was willing to be subservient to management or the clinicians or the dean just because those individuals might know more about medical care or research and education than did individual board members. Not only did board members ask questions, but a policy was established by management from the beginning that the board members would always be informed, no matter the issue, and that they would be informed in a prompt and efficient manner. This meant that the board, well informed, not only felt engaged but able to make critical decisions from a base of knowledge.

Theme Four—Academic Hospital Ownership is Not a Government Function

The fourth theme is that certain functions are not inherently governmental functions—owning and running a hospital is one of them. The story here is how a mediocre medical institution, run like the state entity which it was, still ran deficits no matter how much state money was invested. This resulted in a poor physical plant and unsatisfying conditions for all. The simple fact is that most government-run hospitals are structured in such a way that there are no incentives to bill and collect, to prioritize, and to convert its collections into renewal of technology and facilities or into quality and safety. The basic issue is that a government does not run a hospital to be efficient, high quality and competitive in the same manner that independent hospitals must do.

Other states faced issues similar to those that existed in Maryland and made somewhat similar decisions. For example, Florida, West Virginia and Arizona all privatized their hospitals about the same time that the University of Maryland Medical System was created. A number of private universities did likewise, for example, the University of Chicago privatized its hospital in the early 1990s.

The Baltimore City Hospital had become essentially a failing indigent care hospital on the east side of town. Under Mayor Schaefer, the hospital and its surrounding land were turned over to Johns Hopkins University and Johns Hopkins Hospital. Over time this has resulted in a modern, effective institution (Johns Hopkins Bayview Hospital) which is now being so recognized across the city. It is worth noting here that in that turnover, the then-mayor assured that the personnel system conversion was done more effectively than had been done by the State of Maryland at UMMS. Indeed, when Schaefer became governor, he recalled the issues and needs at Baltimore City Hospital and this background helped him to understand the issues and to assist UMMS to correct its personnel system.

States have always had a major function in running mental hospitals. The issues that have been raised above still apply in that setting, but in this situation, to a large degree, government runs these hospitals by default. There is simply no place else that is available for anyone who has less than excellent insurance or substantial wealth.

For years the Veterans Administration hospitals had a mediocre reputation. Care procedures moved slowly, and the general perception was that care at a Veterans hospital was not as good as in community hospitals. But that has changed in recent years. Veterans Administration hospitals have, indeed, become the role models in the country for patient safety, quality management, universal use of EMRs and early universal digitization of radiology. The Veterans Administration has demonstrated that a government agency can operate a hospital effectively. It is worth noting, however, that the VA appreciates its hospitals as one of its major if not most important functions and hence devotes the necessary leadership, management and resources along with appropriate policies and procedures to assure that these hospitals will indeed meet the standards which the nation has set for the care of its veterans.

The Veterans Administration example makes it clear that some government agencies have found ways to operate hospitals effectively, but most often this does not happen simply because government, such as a state, does not separate out the hospital from the approaches used elsewhere in state government. Nor does government embed in it the necessary policies and procedures to operate in a competitive environment where consumers, payers, and physicians will go elsewhere if not satisfied. In a number of states, including Maryland, the decision was to separate the hospital from state ownership and university governance while creating linkages that would maintain the mission of the hospital to be consistent with the needs of the state's medical school. In Maryland, separation was essential but not sufficient for success. To this was added, over time, alignment, leadership, vision, entrepreneurism, and a pubic–private partnership to recapitalize.

Some have suggested that the structure created by the legislature in 1984 was not the best. The authors would argue that many different structures can be effective. But it is the people, the vision and the alignment that in the end make for success. Each leader as part of the partnership must demonstrate effective leadership. In the case of the University of Maryland Medical System, separate governance was essential for success, but it was definitely not sufficient. Success depended ultimately on the physicians since they built the programs. To be sure, the medical system provided financial, planning and organizational assistance, along with a commitment of many staff members of the medical system to make the programs work. But the physicians were the key to program development. Success also depended upon the medical school. The school created the opportunity for research-based clinical care that attracted new patients to a developing tertiary care center. So, all in all, it is a matter of alignment. To the extent that alignment existed over the years from 1984 on, there has been success.

Sometimes alignment has not been present. When alignment between the medical system and the physicians lapsed for a period in the late 1980s tensions were exacerbated, with the chiefs in effect demanding change. Again, from 2004 to 2008, alignment was diminished with both the physicians and with the medical school, and impaired and impeded the growth and effectiveness of the medical system as well as the growth and effectiveness of the medical school. A return to extensive efforts at alignment beginning in 2008 has once again reinvigorated the partnership with the school and its faculty physicians while reconnecting with the leadership of the state government to assure ongoing capital access for the medical center's facilities renewal. It has also encouraged outsiders to look favorably on the medical system as a potential merger partner and will likely lead to other advantages in the years to come.

Another Element of Leadership

The four themes of this book are important but do not, however, impart another principle—leaders need to be involved and caring. Alignment, entrepreneurial management and strategy are essential. But so too is an abiding belief that all hospitals exist to give care, and academic hospitals exist to give care, teach the next generation of providers and enable research for the future. If caring comes first then a caring staff is essential, and the leaders must care as well. We tried to demonstrate our caring by simple means such as picking up dropped stuff from the floor, pushing a patient in a wheelchair, visiting patients, just prowling the halls, all the while talking to nurses and housekeepers and being generally available both in and out of the office. We made plenty of decisions that some did not like; we hope that most recognize that they were only made to advance the agenda as we saw it—to heal, to teach, to discover.

-*Stephen C. Schimpff MD and Morton I. Rapoport MD*

The story of the medical system in this book has been about birth and maturation; but the story is certainly not over. Indeed, UMMS is now just reaching maturity and has great potential for the future. This is a revolutionary period for health care, and change nationally is in the air. The ability to diagnose, treat, and prevent illness is advancing at a truly incredible rate, with the medical system and the medical school at the forefront of discovery and application of new modalities of care. But on the delivery of care side, medical costs are too high; patient care is not adequately coordinated; quality and safety are less than desirable; indeed the entire delivery system needs to be addressed and modified as appropriate. We have offered some suggestions for what the medical system—with its partner the medical school and the faculty physicians—might want to consider thereby becoming national leaders in this agenda. But whatever transpires, the opportunities are limitless.

LESSONS LEARNED:

The authors' observation and principal suggestion is that a university and a hospital system can and should—indeed, must—work together, to better each other and provide a unified "face" to the local, regional, and national public community. This requires that the leaders must recognize the imperative and be prepared to live it, to put the institution above personal agendas and to recognize that the combined success of the two institutions is the only way that each can have true success. Organizational structure is important—but only committed leadership that constantly addresses alignment can assure success.

To this suggestion are corollary suggestions that alignment with other critical parties is equally important. In the medical system's case it was the state government, the rate setting commission, the banking community, potential donors and friends and many others. Together, they all made up a vertical spine that was able to stand straight and yield much good for the populace.

Finally, these are lessons that apply to all AMCs, but also to hospitals in general where alignment with the community physicians is essential for effective program development and sustainability. And the concept of alignment should not be lost on most businesses. Certainly hospitals must depend on others (principally physicians) to bring in revenue (patients), but so too must many businesses depend on others having a unity of strategy and priorities to assure that business plans proceed as desired.

Index